T0175533

Zhihua Wang
Kefa Cen
Junhu Zhou
Jianren Fan

Simultaneous Multi-Pollutants Removal in Flue Gas by Ozone

Zhihua Wang
Kefa Cen
Junhu Zhou
Jianren Fan

Simultaneous Multi-Pollutants Removal in Flue Gas by Ozone

With 45 figures

ZHEJIANG UNIVERSITY PRESS
浙江大学出版社

Springer

Authors
Prof. Zhihua Wang
State Key Laboratory of Clean Energy
  Utilization
Zhejiang University
Hangzhou 310027, China
E-mail: wangzh@zju.edu.cn

Prof. Junhu Zhou
State Key Laboratory of Clean Energy
  Utilization
Zhejiang University
Hangzhou 310027, China
E-mail: enejhzhou@public.zju.edu.cn

Prof. Kefa Cen
State Key Laboratory of Clean Energy
  Utilization
Zhejiang University
Hangzhou 310027, China
E-mail: kfcen@zju.edu.cn

Prof. Jianren Fan
State Key Laboratory of Clean Energy
  Utilization
Zhejiang University
Hangzhou 310027, China
E-mail: fanjr@zju.edu.cn

ISSN 1995-6819   e-ISSN 1995-6827
Advanced Topics in Science and Technology in China

ISBN 978-7-308-13258-9
Zhejiang University Press, Hangzhou

ISBN 978-3-662-43513-7   e-ISBN 978-3-662-43514-4
Springer Heidelberg New York Dordrecht London

Library of Congress Control Number: 2014939022

Printed on acid-free paper

Springer is part of Springer Science+Business Media (www.springer.com)

Preface

Despite the rapid development in clean energy technologies, such as hydrogen fuel, wind and solar energy, the majority of the energy consumption in a foreseeable future will still rely on combustion technologies using fossil fuels, waste and biomass. It is well known that pollutant emissions including NO_x, SO_2, mercury, volatile organic compounds (VOCs), and dioxins from combustion and incineration processes of coal, biomass, municipal solid waste (MSW), and different kinds of waste, are extraordinary harmful to the atmosphere and human health. In China, coal has been traditionally the major primary energy source, and its role is expected to continue growing in the forecasted period. Under these circumstances, pollutant emissions derived from coal combustion have inevitably become prominent.

So far, a variety of possible options already existing to reduce these emissions individually are proposed and carried out, but unfortunately, each pollutant control method individually is turned out to be not only high investment, but also decreases the whole system reliability. Therefore, actively developing research on the coal-fired multi-pollutants removal and exploring an advanced, reliable, and cost-effective multi-pollutants removal technology are remarkably hot issues for Chinese sustainable development in light of the current use of coal as main energy source.

Ozone injection is one of the most promising multi-pollutants simultaneous removal technologies with high efficiency, energy saving, and low cost, because the strongly oxidizing radicals such as O_3, O, OH, and O_2^* are generated in flue gas after ozone injection. These radicals actively convert NO_x into NO_2 and transform elemental mercury into its oxidized form (such as HgO and $HgCl_2$), both of which are of thoroughly water-soluble. Integrated with the existing WFGD (wet flue gas desulfurization) system and special designed alkali absorption tower, pollutants including NO_x, SO_2, Hg, VOCs, and dioxin could be removed simultaneously.

By presenting a number of fundamental research findings, significant scientific breakthroughs, and novel advances in the research field of multi-pollutants removal by ozone during the last decades, this book will provide the readers with updated information in the field of air pollution control technology related to the coal-fired power plants. Furthermore, the fundamental research findings, comprised of the detail reaction mechanism between ozone and flue gas components, are obtained not only from chemical kinetics modeling but also from lab-scale experimental investigations. The demonstration case of the multi-pollutants removal by ozone will be attentively employed to conduct, with the help of the detailed reaction mechanism obtained. In short, this book remains at the fore front of research and development in this crucial area related with multi-pollutants removal by ozone injection.

The book is logically divided into the following five chapters.

Chapter 1 gives an overview of the state-of-art development of coal-fired pollution control technologies. It refers to various control technologies for sulfur dioxide, nitrogen oxides, mercury, VOCs as well as dioxin and flue gas multi-pollutants simultaneous removal technologies.

Chapter 2 presents the removal technology of multi-pollutants in flue gas by ozone oxidation. The physical and chemical properties of ozone are summarized. Ozone generation methods and overviews on the progress of ozone synthesis technologies with discharge plasma are described as well.

Chapter 3 elucidates in detail the chemical kinetics mechanism between O_3 and $NO_x/SO_2/Hg$, which stems from chemical kinetic modeling and lab-scale experimental invetigations. The chemical kinetics model considers 40 typical species in flue gas and refers to 121 elementary reactions in total.

Chapter 4 provides the simultaneous removal mechanism of multi-pollutants with ozone and wet scrubbing, which is obtained from lab-scale experimental work. It is attached extremely importance to the NO_2 absorption in a wet scrubber for achieving an optimal NO_x removal. Accordingly, key operational parameters that can affect the NO_2 removal are to take into account and effects of the pH value and initial $NO/SO_2/S(IV)$ concentration are determined.

In Chapter 5, the work on the ozone multi-pollutants control associated with wet scrubber system has effectively led to the development of an oxidation-absorber system that is undergoing demonstration and commercialization. An economic analysis of the system is involved and highly needed for future commercialization.

This work was financed by the National Natural Science Foundation of China (Nos. 51176169 & 51390491), the key project of the Chinese National Programs for Fundamental Research and Development (No. 2012CB214906) and National Science Foundation for Distinguished Young Scholars (No. 50525620).

The authors have benefited enormously from the interaction and contributions of the other members of the group. Essentially, the book covers the experience and findings gained by the other working team in the related research field.

As a final note, we wish to thank all the authors for their participation in making this book possible. And we are especially grateful to the other members of our group. We also want to thank Dr. Zhengcheng Wen, Dr. Xiang Zhang, Dr. Min Kuang, Dr. Yong He, Dr. Shudong Jiang, Dr. Lv Yu, Dr. Xin Hu, Dr. Zhuo You, Dr. Xiaoye Liang, Dr. Pei He, Dr. Yajun Zhou, Miss Daili Li, Mr. Chaoqun Xu for contributions on managing and copy-editing the context of this special issue.

The authors
Hangzhou, China
Mar., 2014

Contents

1

Development of Pollution Control Technology During Coal Combustion

1.1 Introduction

As we are moving ahead into the 21st century, our hunger for cost-effective and environmentally friendly energy continues to grow. The energy information administration of US has forecasted that only in the first two decades of the 21st century, our energy demand will increase by 60% compared to the levels at the end of the 20th century. Fossil fuels have been traditionally the major primary energy sources worldwide, and their role is expected to continue growing for the forecasted period, due to their inherent cost competitiveness compared to non-fossil fuel energy sources. However, the current fossil energy scenario is undergoing significant transformations, especially to accommodate increasingly stringent environmental challenges of contaminants like sulfur dioxide, nitrogen oxides or mercury, while still providing affordable energy [1]. In China, coal has been traditionally the major primary energy sources, and its role is expected to continue growing for the forecasted period, due to Chinese energy consumption structure and its inherent cost competitiveness compared to other fossil or non-fossil fuel energy sources [2].

The economy of China has been growing rapidly, and the living conditions of people have been improved significantly in the past three decades. However, with the development of the economy, the energy consumption has increased and the environmental pollution has inevitably become prominent.

As a primary source of energy, coal is mainly used for direct combustion. While, the traditional coal combustion is inherently plagued with a large amount of atmospheric pollutants, especially soot, SO_2, NO_x [3], CO/CO_2, volatile organic compounds (VOCs) [4], Hg and other trace toxic heavy metals [5,6], dioxins, and strong carcinogens. These pollutants irrefutably damage to the atmospheric and ecological environments and jeopardize human health.

On the basis of the statistics of National Environmental Protection Administration, 80% of soot emission, 90% of SO_2 emission, 67% of NO_x emissions, 90% of CO_2 emission and 40% of mercury emission of the total were extremely derived from the direct combustion of coal in China [7]. The state-of-date and the strictest emission limitations (GB13223-2011) in coal-fired power plant was promulgated and taken into force in 2012 in China. Thus, it is more likely that coal energy producers would adapt to the new requirements by developing and implementing emission control technologies.

1.2   Existing Air Pollution Control Technologies

It is well known that emissions including SO_2, NO_x, mercury, VOCs, and dioxins from coal combustion are extraordinary harmful to our atmosphere. In china, coal has been traditionally the major primary energy sources, and its role is expected to continue growing for the forecasted period, emission derived from coal combustion has inevitably become prominent. Thus, developing the existing air pollution control technologies and exploring the reasonable, high-effective alternative would be a hot issue and attached great importance.

So far, a variety of possible options already existing to reduce these emissions individually were proposed and carried out, whereas a simultaneous multi-pollutants removal technology during coal combustion in China is absent up to now and put forward in this book.

1.2.1   Desulfurization Technology

Approaches to control SO_2 emission of coal-fired boiler mainly include pre-combustion, combustion, and post-combustion desulfurization. A brief introduction to major desulphurization technologies is presented below.

1.2.1.1   Circulating Fluidized-Bed Technology

Fluidized-bed combustion (FBC) technology first appeared in the 1960s [8], followed by circulating FBC. Limestone or dolomite is mainly used as desulfurizer for this technology. During the coal combustion process, the limestone or dolomite is decomposed into CaO, which reacts with O_2 and SO_2 in the oxidizing atmosphere to form $CaSO_4$. Circulating Fluidized-bed technology is widely used in the world, because of the characteristics of fuel flexibility, high combustion efficiency, and low pollution emissions.

1.2.1.2   Wet Flue-Gas Desulfurization Technology

Wet flue-gas desulfurization (WFGD) technology, which is based on using limestone or lime as a reagent, is a wet scrubbing process and has been the most frequently selected flue-gas desulfurization (FGD) technology for SO_2 reduction from coal-fired utility boilers [9]. The WFGD flue gas treatment system is typically located after removal of particulate matter from flue gas either by a baghouse or an electrostatic precipitator (ESP). The cleaned flue gas is then discharged to the stack. SO_2 is removed by scrubbing flue gas with either a limestone or lime (reagent) slurry. Nowadays, WFGD, which is considered to be a commercially mature technology, has been applied widely in coal-fired power plants globally.

In most WFGD systems, the quantity of liquid sprayed relative to flue gas is related to the SO_2 collection efficiency needed and is referred to as liquid-to-gas (L/G) ratio. Higher L/G ratios improve SO_2 removal by exposing the gas to more absorbing liquid, implying that higher L/G ratios also consume more power.

Conclusively, the WFGD technology has such features as highly efficient desulfurization (achieving more than 95% SO_2 cleanup) and high operation cost.

1.2.1.3   Spray Dry Flue-Gas Desulfurization Technology

Alkaline solution or hydrated lime emulsion is usually employed as desulfurizer for the spray dry flue-gas desulfurization process [10]. Considering that the wet desulfurization agent is used but the dry final product is generated, this method is also called the semi-dry desulfurization technology. The rotary spray desulfurization technology is currently widely adopted by most countries especially municipal solid waste incineration power plants because of its reliable operation, no fouling and plugging, and easy handling of solid products. Moreover, this technology seems to be more economical and efficient in retrofitting the existing power plants than WFGD.

1.2.1.4 Calcium Injection/Humidification Desulfurization Technology in Furnace

Limestone, dolomite, and hydrated lime are typically used as desulfurizers, which are decomposed into CaO for SO_2 absorption [11]. The Alanco Company in the United States provides a charged spray dry absorbent device for dust removal and desulfurization system [12]. This device allows a high-speed absorbent flow through a high-voltage electrostatic-corona charging zone generated by the spray unit, so that the absorber carries strong electrostatic charge. As the absorber flows into the sooty flue gas, the electrical charges will exclude the particles with each another. Therefore, a uniform distribution with suspended state is then formed to produce a sufficient reaction between the absorbent and SO_2. This technology approves lower investment and small space needed, and is suitable for retrofitting old plants. However, the high technical demands and complex maintenance of this technology limit its application.

1.2.1.5 Electron-Beam (E-Beam) FGD Technology

The e-beam FGD technology is adopted for injecting NH_3 into flue gas, which is then irradiated by e-beam [13,14]. Therefore, SO_x and NO_x in flue gas react with NH_3 to generate $(NH_4)_2SO_4$ and NH_4NO_3. This desulfurization technology is competitive and has the following main features: (i) It is simple and can realize desulfurization and denitrification efficiently and simultaneously; (ii) The entire desulfurization process does not require post-treatment of wastewater; (iii) $(NH_4)_2SO_4$ and NH_4NO_3, which are the by-products of the reaction, are considered as raw materials of compound fertilizer production; (iv) This technology occupies small space and is a good alternative either for retrofitting old plants or newly-built units; (v) After treatment, flue gas can be directly released into the atmosphere; (vi) It requires relatively lower investment and operation cost.

1.2.1.6 Seawater FGD Technology

Seawater is commonly used as desulfurization agent for absorbing SO_2 through the seawater FGD technology [15]. The process of this technology is relatively simple, mainly including a spray absorber tower and an aeration tank. Flue gas reacts with seawater in the spray tower, which is then restored in the aeration tank. This technology has several advantages. For example, it does not require the preparation or addition of a desulfurizer and is reliable with low investment and operation cost, in addition to no wastewater and waste materials needed to be disposed. Consequently, this technology has received considerable attention all over the world and is now operating or under construction in Norway, Spain, Indonesia, United Kingdom, USA, and other countries.

1.2.2 Denitrification Technology

Methods for controlling NO_x emissions are usually classified into two categories: combustion $deNO_x$ and post-combustion $deNO_x$ technologies. The combustion $deNO_x$ method is applied to diminish NO_x formation through the low-oxygen combustion, staged-air combustion, re-burning, and flue-gas recirculation by adjusting the primary air and secondary air distribution and changing the combustion conditions in the furnace. The post-combustion $deNO_x$ method utilizes reagents to reduce NO_x in the flue gas. Selective catalytic reduction (SCR) and selective non-catalytic reduction (SNCR) are usually used and involved in this category. The following content provides a brief introduction on denitrification technologies.

1.2.2.1 Low-Oxygen Combustion Technology

As to the low-oxygen combustion technology, combustion is kept at a low excess air coefficient, both limited oxygen fed into the reaction zone and relative low flame temperature can inhibit the generation of fuel NO_x and thermal NO_x on the basis of the oxygen-sensitive characteristics of fuel NO_x.

NO_x emissions can be reduced by 15% – 20% through this method. However, if the excess air coefficient is too low during the real operations, the combustion stability will be seriously jeopardized. Consequently, the flame center will moved up and emissions such as CO, soot, and fly ash will increase rapidly, which will irrefutably lead to dangerous boiler operation conditions.

1.2.2.2   Staged-Air Combustion Technology

The staged-air combustion technology obtains the minimum NO_x formation by forming oxygen-lean, fuel-rich regions in the main combustion zone through a multi-level air supply strategy. The injected over-fire air (OFA) makes the pulverized coal to be burnt out. The parameters which impact on the NO_x removal efficiency are the excessive air ratio, temperature, and residence time in the main combustion zone. The excess air ratio in the main combustion zone generally ranges from 0.7 to 0.95. The temperature and residence time mostly depend on the excess air ratio in the primary combustion zone.

This method is quite simple and effective for either the existing or newly built boilers. Compared with the outdated boiler models, the advanced, integrated-air staging combustion technology can reduce NO_x by 15% – 30% [16]. However, it may possibly cause corrosion and slag in the furnace, along with a reduction in the combustion efficiency.

1.2.2.3   Flue-Gas Recirculation

Flue-gas recirculation is one of a low-NO_x combustion technology, widely employed for gas-fired and oil-fired boilers. It introduces the re-circulate flue gas into the combustion zone by using a fan to lower the flame temperature and to dilute the oxygen concentration so as to reduce the NO_x formation.

Gas mixing and fuel combustion can be significantly improved by flue-gas recirculation. Thus, NO emissions can be reduced by about 20%. However, this method barely inhibits thermal NO_x generation. If the circulating flue gas exceeds to 15 wt.% of the combustion air, the NO_x reduction will eventually decrease a lot. The maximum flue gas recycled is limited by the flame stability. Recirculation fans must be added once retrofitting is necessary. Flue-gas recycling and modification is relatively easy and the retrofit investment is low.

1.2.2.4   Reburning Technology

Reburning [17] is an effective and promising alternative method for reducing NO_x emissions. Reburning technology can reduce NO_x emissions by 50% – 70%, which is inferior to SCR and SNCR. Reburning can keep a stable reductive atmosphere in the fuel-rich zone, low excess air ratio area, high concentrations of

NH_x, CH_x, and CO, as well as longer residence time of flue gas in the reduction zone, thereby reducing NO_x.

The technology is based on the utilization of hydrocarbon radicals, i.e., CH, HCN, and NH_3, and other radicals decomposed from reburning fuel, to reduce NO_x. Fuel is fed into the furnace in stage, and the reburning fuel is injected at the top of the flame to establish a fuel-rich zone and to deoxygenize the generated NO_x. The OFA is then injected to ensure complete combustion. Generally, 80% – 85% of fuel (known as the primary fuel) is introduced into the main combustion zone and burned out with the excess air. The remaining 15% – 20% of fuel (known as the reburning fuel) is sent into the upper part of the main burner (reburning zone) to form a reductive atmosphere for converting NO into N_2. The pulverized coal and natural gas are usually considered as reburning fuels. However, the latter is superior to the former in terms of NO_x reduction. Generally, the optimum NO_x reduction efficiency with acceptable burnout levels can reach up to 50%.

1.2.2.5 SCR

The SCR method [18] is developed based on the fact that a number of reagents can directly convert NO_x into N_2 and H_2O through metal catalyst at a relatively low temperature. NH_3 is a typical reducing agent that can be sprayed into the flue gas between economizer and air pre-heater. A mixture of NH_3 and flue gas goes through the catalyst bed and undergoes the following reactions:

$$4NH_3+4NO+O_2=4N_2+6H_2O \tag{1.1}$$
$$4NH_3+2NO_2+O_2=3N_2+6H_2O \tag{1.2}$$

Reaction time, flue-gas temperature, flow rate, and NH_3/NO mole ratio are the main parameters affecting NO_x removal efficiency. When $NH_3/NO=1$, the deNO$_x$ of SCR is approximately 80% – 90%. Metal-based and C-based catalysts can also be used [19]. The most common metal-based catalysts are V_2O_5 and TiO_2, and their corresponding operating temperature is approximately 300 – 400 °C. C-based catalysts aim to remove NO_x and SO_2 at the same time, in which C is used to absorb SO_2. The operation temperature of C-based catalysts is about 200 – 250 °C, which is lower than that of metal-based catalysts. The operation temperature of C-based catalysts has a passive effect on deNO$_x$ and enhances the SO_2 adsorption.

1.2.2.6   SNCR

In the SNCR [20] technology, a NH_x-based reducing agent (mainly ammonia and urea) is injected into the furnace zone where the temperature range is around 800 – 1100 °C. NO_x is rapidly converted into N_2 and H_2O. The chemical reaction in this technology is nearly the same as that occurring in the SCR technology, except that the former has no catalyst demand. The denitrification effect mainly depends on the temperature distribution in the spray area. The reduction reaction usually begins to faint at temperatures below 900 °C, resulting in a lower NO removal and NH_3 leakage. When the temperature is too high, NH_3 is naturally oxidized into NO, resulting in high NO_x emissions. Therefore, an appropriate temperature range for maintaining high $deNO_x$ and sumptuously avoiding the NH_3 leakage, should be considered in the SNCR NH_3-injection technology [21]. It is found out that the NO_x removal with SNCR in an entrained-flow reactor, under the conditions of $n(N)/n(NO_x) = 1.5$, 900 – 1000 °C, and residence time of 2 s, and using urea reductant, 70% – 80% NO removal and 45% – 50% NO_2 removal were obtained, and the N_2O is below 7×10^{-6} [22]. In real-furnace application, for pulverized-coal boilers with 1100 – 1200 °C at the furnace outlet, around 40% of NO_x can be reduced due to the short resident time at the selected temperature window. For a CFB boiler with the combustion chamber running at around 850 – 950 °C, the flue gas passage between the cyclone and combustion chamber is the suitable position for the SNCR reaction. With a well mixing process in the cyclone, the NO_x reduction efficiency can usually reach 70%.

1.2.2.7   Advanced Reburning Technology

The advanced reburning technology integrates the traditional SNCR technology with reburning to further reduce NO_x. This technology can reduce NO_x by more than 85% and is much more economical than that of SCR. Shortly, the advanced reburning technology is one of the most attractive denitrification technologies [23] and comprehensive investigations have been reported [24–26]. The NH_3-injection position varies with the SNCR technology. NH_3 is sprayed into the oxidation region after OFA in the traditional SNCR technology, but the NH_3-sprayed procedure quite differs within the advanced reburning technology. The advanced reburning technology can be divided into three forms on the basis of the relationship between the NH_3 injection location and the reburning zone, i.e., the advanced reburning lean technology, advanced reburning rich technology, and multiple-injection advanced reburning technology [27–29].

1.2.2.8 Oxygen-Enhanced Combustion

In the oxygen-enhanced combustion technology, pure O_2 is injected into low-NO_x burners or OFA to replace air. Deep-staging technologies can be applied to create a strong reductive atmosphere to reduce NO_x emissions. The coal combustion intensity will decline and less heat will be released by using low-NO_x burners and OFA for forming air-staging conditions, which decrease the chemical equivalent of the main combustion zone. This phenomenon often results in a less flame stability, lower flame temperature, and higher carbon in fly ash. These factors tend to limit the air-staging degree. When O_2 is applied, the staging degree can be significantly improved given the superior performance of pure oxygen combustion. Consequently, the chemical equivalent ratio of burners can be 0.85 or even lower. While the flame temperature increases, the combustion stability will improve, and the decomposition rate of volatile N will increase at an early stage to generate low NO_x emissions. Compared with air staging, carbon in fly ash under pure oxygen combustion conditions will be significantly reduced. Results of Praxair Corporation in a 44-MWe industrial furnace show that the oxygen-enhanced combustion can effectively improve the staging intensity of low-NO_x burners and reduce carbon in fly ash and flue-gas opacity, compared with air staging [30]. Moreover, in an experiment with replacing 5% of the combustion air by O_2, a 40% NO_x reduction was achieved. Numerical results of the Praxair's oxygen-enhanced combustion technology [31] suggested that replacing 2% of air with O_2 could reduce about 35% of NO_x emissions without a significant increase in burnout rate and no obvious change appeared in the slagging rate on water-cooling walls.

1.2.2.9 Hybrid Selective Reduction Technology

In recent years, new NO_x control hybrid systems, using a combination of SNCR and SCR technology, have been developed. These hybrid systems reduce levels of nitrogen oxides in fossil fuel combustion flue gas with a selective non-catalytic reduction treatment stage followed by a selective catalytic reduction treatment stage. The hybrid SNCR/SCR technology can be a cost effective compromise with the SNCR and SCR system, reducing NO_x, and balancing capital and operation cost.

In a high-temperature area, the SNCR technology reduces NO_x by injecting NH_3. The unreacted NH_3 further reacts with NO_x with the aid of a catalyst arranged at the later zone with low temperatures. This hybrid technology utilizes SNCR by increasing the dose of the reducing agent. NH_3 leakage can be controlled and reused during the SCR process. The SCR catalysts can also be arranged inside the flue gas duct to save the capital cost. No additional catalyst tower construction is needed. Therefore, the investment and operation cost of this hybrid technology are lower than those of the SCR technology. The application of the hybrid selective reduction technology in 320 MWe units in the Mercer Generating Station power plant suggested that a 90% NO_x reduction could be achieved and the NH_3 leakage was less than 10 ppm [32]. Additionally, catalyst-loaded air preheaters have been developed by some companies to utilize the unreacted NH_3, thereby effectively reducing the NH_3 leakage.

1.2.3   Hg Removal Technology

Coal-fired power plants are generally taken as the major anthropogenic emission source of mercury. Normally, mercury speciation in flue gas is classified into three forms, i.e., gaseous elemental mercury (Hg^0), gaseous oxidized mercury (Hg^{2+}), and particulate mercury ($Hg_{(p)}$). Gaseous mercury, which consists of elemental and oxidized mercury, accounts for about 86.5% – 97.8% of the total mercury emission. Generally, Hg^{2+} is water soluble, apt to absorb by wet scrubber. However, Hg^0 is relatively difficult to be controlled, owing to higher volatility, insensitive to water-solubility and a stable speciation, which cause global mercury pollution with the help of atmospheric motion.

In general, the Hg-removal efficiency greatly depends on the mercury speciation existing in flue gas. Various factors affect the mercury speciation distribution, such as the type of coal used, gas temperature, combustion manner, pollutant control devices, fly ash composition, and flue-gas composition like chloride, NO, and SO_2.

Control methods of coal-fired mercury emission can be divided into three categories: (i) mercury control technologies before combustion, such as coal washing and drying technologies which are not commonly used in industry; (ii) mercury control technologies during combustion, which are focused on improving combustion methods and developing additives; and (iii) mercury control technologies after combustion, i.e. utilizing various absorbents, the existing pollution control devices, and de-Hg technologies to achieve the mercury removal. Typical de-Hg technologies contain the corona discharge plasma technology and multi-pollutants removal technology by ozone oxidation.

1.2.3.1 Absorbent

Currently, more and more studies have focused on adopting activated carbon and other adsorbents for mercury removal [33]. However, the mercury absorption mechanism by using activated carbon remains unclear. Absorbents and the related adsorption performance have been extensively reported in the literature, which mainly include activated carbon [34], fly ash [35], calcium-based absorbent [36], mineral substance-based absorbent [37], zeolite-based catalytic adsorbent [38], and precious metal-based adsorbent [39].

1.2.3.2 Coal-Washing or Coal Drying Technology

Coal washing and drying are effective methods for eliminating mercury before combustion [40]. Generally, coal washing is divided into two categories. One is based on the different specific gravity to separate impurities, such as dense-medium separators and cyclones. The other utilizes different physical and chemical properties of coal surface, involving the coal-flotation and oil-flocculation technologies. The mercury removal rate of the flotation technology, with a mean value ranging from 21% – 37%, depends on the coal type, method of washing, and mercury concentration in coal. Generally, a coal drying technology can obtain a higher mercury removal of about 70%. Actually, both coal washing and drying are out-of-dated technologies and therefore are hardly to be taken into practice in industry, despite a considerable mercury removal accomplished.

1.2.3.3 Conventional Pollution Control Device

Mercury control technologies after combustion refer to mercury removal from the coal-fired flue gas. Besides the absorbent method in flue gas, using the existing conventional flue gas pollution control devices to reduce mercury emission is considered as a cost-effective alternative way. Currently, the existing flue gas pollution control devices contain the FGD, particle-control equipment (ESP or fabric filter), NO_x-control equipment (SCR). In view of the high water-solubility of oxidized mercury compounds (such as $HgCl_2$), the WFGD system can remove 80% – 95% of Hg^{2+} [41]. Hg^0 is very difficult to be removed because of its high volatility and particularly low water-solubility. However, Hg^0 in flue gas can be oxidized into Hg^{2+} by the SCR catalysts in the existing denitration equipment. This enables the Hg^0 abatement to be achieved in coal-fired power plants. The mercury removal efficiency of such an equipment depends on the mercury speciation distribution in flue gas, which is ultimately affected by the coal type.

1.2.3.4   Corona Discharge Plasma Technology

As a new mercury removal method, the corona discharge plasma technology is keeping developed. Using a narrow pulsed-corona discharge method, Wu and Urabe [42] conducted an industrial test to remove the Hg vapor in the 10 m^3/h flue gas of a waste incinerator. It was found that the removal efficiency deceased with the gas temperature and related with the gas residence time in the electric field, pulse voltage frequency, and corona power. When the initial Hg vapor concentration reached 2 mg/m^3, the removal efficiency achieved 100% under certain conditions. The existing HCl gas could also improve the removal efficiency. The removal principles relied on that the Hg vapor was oxidized by O atoms and O_3 in the corona discharge field. The related oxidation reactions are as follows.

$$Hg+O=HgO \qquad (1.3)$$
$$Hg+O_3=HgO+O_2 \qquad (1.4)$$
$$Hg+2Cl^-=HgCl_2 \qquad (1.5)$$

Since the mercury concentration in typical coal-fired flue gas is very low, the absorption of oxidized mercury is not easy. Again, considering the high cost and running fee, the corona discharge plasma technology is still not put into commercial application in coal-fired boilers to remove mercury.

1.2.3.5   Semi-Dry Based Hg Removal Technology

A more-effective semi-dry mercury removal technology specially for coal-fired flue gas has been proposed recently by the Institute for Thermal Power Engineering, Zhejiang University. This technology, designed to remove mercury together with SO_2 emission [43–46], comprises several steps. At the beginning, the absorbent is injected into the furnace zone with gas temperature ranging from 800 – 900 °C and into the flue gas passage, respectively. The ratio of absorbent to mercury concentration is kept around 600 – 1600. The particulate mercury can be successfully trapped by the ESP or fabric filter. Then, the oxidation process takes place, which converts elementary mercury into oxidized mercury at 150 – 160 °C. The oxidized mercury can be absorbed in the following wet scrubber. The bench- and pilot-scale experimental results have confirmed that both the gaseous and particulate mercury in flue gas could be eliminated by as high as 85% [47]. This approved the potential to put into practice in the further demonstration and industrial applications.

1.2.4   VOCs Control Technology

VOCs are organic liquids and solids that have vapor pressures greater than 70.91 Pa at room temperature and have boiling points below 260 °C in air. VOCs emissions regarded as the second largest category of atmospheric pollutant (following the dust pollutant) mainly come from chemical companies, waste incinerations, and insignificant pollution sources including household combustion, paintings and coatings, etc. VOCs control has attracted a lot of attention because of its serious harm to human health. However, the existing control technologies seem to be unsatisfied, specifically for the huge volume of flue gas with very low VOCs concentration. Until now, cost-effective methods are still not being applied in power plants.

VOCs control technology can be divided into two categories, namely, the separation and transformation methods [48]. The former separates organic matters from gas including condensation, absorption, adsorption, and membrane-separation methods. The latter converts organic matters into harmless CO_2 and H_2O, including (i) thermal incineration and catalytic combustion methods and (ii) biological, photochemical, and electrochemical degradation technologies. In practice, impact factors such as characteristics of pollutant species, conditions of production, and purification requirements should be considered.

1.2.4.1   Adsorption Method

The adsorption method is one of the most common methods for controlling VOCs[49]. The adsorption efficiency is extremely attributed to the adsorption characteristics of the adsorbent, which means that the adsorbent must embody a strong selective absorption capacity, large surface area, adequate mechanical strength, as well as thermal and chemical stabilities. Considering that a large surface area yields large adsorption capacity, activated carbon, activated carbon fibers, and hydrophobic zeolite that are commonly used in industries, can be applied to deal with organic compounds with a molecular weight 40 – 150 and low boiling point. Although adsorption is a simple, recycling-effective, safe, and reliable method to deal with VOCs, various problems such as a high flow resistance during the adsorption process, high amount of adsorbent and high equipment investment needed, and complicated operations of the absorbent bed, necessitate to be resolved before industrial applications.

1.2.4.2   Catalytic Combustion Technology

Catalytic combustion is one of the most common organic-waste-gas control methods [50]. This method, almost applied to all kinds of organic hydrocarbon waste gas, embraces advantages summarized as follows. Firstly, the cost of the auxiliary fuel required is greatly reduced because of the lower ignition temperature (250 – 450 °C, compared with the 600 – 800 °C of direct combustion) and energy consumption. Secondly, this method generates no secondary pollution and combustion products (CO_2 and H_2O) with purities above 95%. Moreover, the NO_x formation is largely reduced at the reduced combustion temperature levels. Thirdly, the equipment size is less than one thermal incineration. However, drawbacks of this method include the catalyst deactivation and limited flue gas treatment.

1.2.4.3   Biological Control Technology

Organic matters are energies or nutrients of microbial survival produced through microbial metabolism [51], which can be eventually translated into simple inorganic matters and cell components. Biological control technology has three forms, namely, biological washing, filtration, and trickling deleted.

Biological control technology has several advantages, such as less secondary pollution generated, simple equipment requirements, low investment, and low operation cost. When handling low VOCs concentrations and good biodegradable gas, this technology is even more promising in terms of economy [52]. However, there exist several disadvantages, such as large covering area, susceptibility to load change, difficult microbial screening, and domestication [53,54]. Given that using a single organic-waste-gas control method always has a number of defects, the hybrid control technology has been developed in recent years, which combines the advantages of various technologies to achieve a low input but high removal efficiency. Current hybrid technologies include the adsorption condensation, catalytic combustion, membrane-based absorption, and so on.

1.3 Simultaneous Multi-Pollutants Removal Technology

So far, a variety of possible options have already existed to reduce these emissions individually. Different kinds of technologies are proposed and carried out, whereas with more and more species needed to be removed, the strategy of one by one control causes not only large investment but also operation cost. Therefore, the research and technology development for a simultaneous multi-pollutants removal become a hot topic all over the world.

The general aim of the simultaneous multi-pollutants control technology is to remove NO_x, SO_2, mercury, and VOCs in one equipment. This book will introduce the current state-of-art controlling technologies for multi-pollutants control in the coal-fired flue gas.

1.3.1 In-Furnace Multi-Pollutants Emission Control Technology

1.3.1.1 O_2/CO_2 Combustion with Ca-Based Sorbent

Okazaki *et al.* [55–57] evaluated the O_2/CO_2 pulverized-coal combustion technology. The practical residence time of SO_2 was extended and SO_2 was enriched inside the furnace because of the application of flue-gas recirculation. Given the high SO_2 concentration, the decomposition of the generated $CaSO_4$ was inhibited. It resulted in the desulfurization efficiency in the O_2/CO_2 combustion system increasing to 4 – 6 times of that in the conventional air combustion system. Meanwhile, the existing high CO_2 conditions inhabited the conversion of fuel-N to NO and parts of the initially generated NO_x were deoxidized during the flue-gas recirculation. Therefore, NO_x emissions reduced greatly. Further removal of SO_2, HCl, and HF could be achieved by the applied Ca-based WFGD system.

1.3.1.2   Low-NO$_x$ Burner Combined with Ca-Based Sorbent

Steward *et al.* [58] studied a low-NO$_x$ burner combined with Ca-based sorbent technique for deNO$_x$ and deSO$_x$ at same time. A desulfurization efficiency of over 50% was achieved at a Ca:S ratio of 2.5 – 3.0. In addition, NO$_x$ emissions were reduced by about 50% by utilizing air-staging conditions. This technique is a typical simple combination of sole methods. The desulfurization and denitrification efficiencies are both relatively low, thus resulting in a poor application in real furnaces.

1.3.1.3   Limestone/Urea Injection in Furnace

Studies on the limestone/urea combined injection technique have been reported widely for deNO$_x$ and deSO$_x$ at same time [59–61]. In this technique, desulfurization is achieved by the limestone injection, while denitrification is obtained by the urea injection based SNCR. Defluorination and dechlorination can also be achieved through an additional Ca-based sorbent. As reported in the literature [61], both desulfurization and denitrification efficiencies reached approximately 80% with Ca/S=2 and NH$_3$/NO=1. Lu [62] concluded that over 90% of SO$_2$ and 80% of NO could be removed by injecting limestone and urea in an entrained-flow reactor at 800 – 1200 °C, with Ca/S=2 and NH$_3$/NO=2.

1.3.1.4   Multi-Pollutants Removal with Organic Calcium Injection

Xiao [63] focused on using organic calcium injection to control SO$_x$ and NO$_x$ simultaneously. The realization of this strategy needs a relatively simple process. The common organic calcium is mainly Ca–Mg acetate (CMA) and calcium acetate. The main principle is that the added organic calcium is decomposed into organic fragments CH$_x$ and CaO. The former can reduce NO directly and the latter can promote heterogeneous reductions of NO by char. CaO itself can remove SO$_2$ in the furnace. Organic calcium develops a high porous structure during its calcinations process at high temperatures, which is helpful to adsorb SO$_2$, HF, HCl, and so on. Therefore, defluorination and dechlorination efficiencies are enhanced accordingly. Xiao [63] found that at the stoichiometric ratio of 1.0 and gas temperature of 1200 °C, denitrification and desulfurization efficiencies reached 73% and 50%, respectively. Results from Nimmo *et al.* [64,65] suggested that using

CMA as a medium, SO_2 and NO could reduced by 70% – 80% and 50% – 80%, respectively, at gas temperature levels of 1100 – 1200 °C within a 80 kWe pulverized-coal boiler. Atal *et al.* [66] found that CMA not only removed SO_2 and NO_x but also strengthened the removal of HF, Hg and sub-particles.

The aforementioned investigations all employ a technique of Ca-based sorbent injection combined with $deNO_x$ combustion conditions to achieve SO_2 and NO_x simultaneously. Major disadvantages of this technique are the medium removal efficiencies and high operation cost of organic calcium. These in-furnace multi-pollutants control technologies, which are efficient in small sized industrial boilers, are hardly to be used in large-scale utility boilers because of the high cost of the large organic calcium consumption and unavailability to meet the increasingly stricter emission legislations.

1.3.2   Flue Gas Multi-Pollutants Emission Control Technology

Compared with the in-furnace combined multi-pollutants removal technology, the flue gas multi-pollutants removal technology usually has a higher efficiency and operation cost. Depicted in recent studies, the post-combustion flue-gas multi-pollutants removal technology can be classified into the following categories.

1.3.2.1   Multi-Pollutants Removal Technology Combined with SCR/SNCR

A combination of various types of sulfur removal technologies (including the Ca-based adsorption, CuO/Al_2O_3 oxidative adsorption, precious metal-catalyzed oxidation, active carbon adsorption technologies, and etc), accompanied with SCR/SNCR, can accomplish a good performance in $deSO_x$ and $deNO_x$ at the same time. However, desulfurization and denitrification are independent with each other. Usually the initial investment and running cost required are mostly high. Several types in this aspect are introduced as below.

Ca-based adsorption combined with SCR/SNCR. Within a called SO_x-NO_x-RO_x-BO_x (SNRB) technology that appearing in the 1990s [67,68], desulfurization, denitrification, and high-temperature dust baghouse can follow a free combination pattern and operate at temperature ranging from 300 – 500 °C. A SNRB technology with annularity SCR catalyst placed in high-temperature baghouse filters, which was developed by Babcock & Wilcox Company, could remove simultaneously NO_x, SO_x, and particulate matters by ejecting a mixture of CaO, $NaHCO_3$, and NH_3 into the upstream flue gas. This multi-pollutants removal technology is rather complicated and less economical, thereby being applied seldom in real furnaces.

CuO/Al_2O_3 oxidization and adsorption combined with SCR/SNCR [69]. Both the desulfurization and denitration reactions of this technique occur in a same unit. The highlight lies in the feature that a γ-Al_2O_3 sorbent impregnated with CuO is used in the desulfurization process. At temperatures ranging from 300 – 500 °C, the sorbent reacts with SO_2 to produce $CuSO_4$. Assisted by the $CuSO_4$ catalysis, NO_x can be reduced by NH_3 ejection. To maintain a recycled process, CuO is finally regenerated by deoxidizing $CuSO_4$ with some reductive gas such as H_2 and CH_4 and the enriched SO_2 product is collected. Apparently, the key point of this technique lies on the high-performance adsorbent preparation. Since 1960s, only a related study from Pittsburg Energy Technology Center has reported a series of test results constructed a small-scale industrial demonstration unit. However, no industrial application has been reported because of its quickly-decreasing sulfur absorption capability after regeneration, poor anti-poison performance, and absorbent abrasion with fly ash.

Precious metal catalytic combined with SCR/SNCR. A so-called SNO_x technology [70–75] belongs to this category. Firstly, fuel gas is heated up to 405 °C and then sent into the SCR unit for reducing NO_x into N_2 through NH_3-based reactions. Thereafter, the flue gas passes through the second reactor where the contained SO_2 transforms into SO_3 through catalytic oxidation, SO_2 will be converted into SO_3. Finally, the flue gas is cooled down by a heat exchanger before passing through a wet scrubber to remove SO_3. Another example is the SNO_x^{TM} technology of ABB Company, in which dual-bed catalytic reactors are used to oxidize SO_2 and reduce NO_x so as to accomplish $deSO_x$ and $deNO_x$ simultaneously. Moreover, the $DESONO_x$ technology developed in a German company, can simultaneously remove SO_2, NO_x, CO, and unburned hydrocarbons at temperatures ranging from 400 – 460 °C. All pollutants in flue gas except NO_x are all disposed through oxidization reactions with precious metals catalysts. That is, CO and unburned hydrocarbons are converted into CO_2 and water, and SO_2 is oxidized into SO_3 before changing to sulfate. It should be noted that precious metal catalysts cannot be absent in both the SNO_x^{TM} and $DESONO_x$ technologies when converting SO_2 and NO_x into SO_3 and NO_2, respectively. These circumstances necessitate high investment and operation cost. Again, in comparison with a conventional multi-pollutants removal technology, here the two types on the one side, do not reduce the amount of devices required, on the other side, are uneconomical to collect the generated diluted sulfuric acid for an efficient utilization.

Activated carbon adsorption combined with SCR/SNCR [76–78]. The basic principles of this type are that in a desulfurization tower, SO_2 is absorbed by activated carbon and then catalytically oxidized into an adsorbed sulfuric acid phase at gas temperatures ranging from 100 – 200 °C. The activated carbon is thereafter injected into separation columns to be regenerated at 350 °C. High concentrations of SO_2 are released accordingly. Then the flue gas enters into a denitration tower where the contained NO_x is reduced into N_2 by the sprayed NH_3, with activated carbon as the catalyst. The desulfurization and denitrification efficiencies reach high levels of above 90% and 70%, respectively. The key factor of this technology is the preparation of activated carbon itself and the loaded active substances. However, this technology turns out unfeasible for large-scale commercial applications because of the high capital cost for the activated carbon preparation. If the cost can be cut down or some alternative can be found, the multi-pollutants removal method will be competitive.

1.3.2.2 Metal-Based Absorbent Multi-Pollutants Removal Technology

This category uses high-efficient metal-based absorbents (integrating metal carriers such as Ca, Na, and Al with various additives) to achieve $deSO_x$ and $deNO_x$ simultaneously. Generally, a high $deSO_2$ efficiency and only a moderate $deNO_x$ level can be achieved, accompanied by high cost in preparing these high-efficient metal-based absorbents. Introductory material about several typical technique cases belonging to this category are listed as below.

Ca-based adsorbent based multi-pollutants removal technology. This type is developed from the advanced silicate (ADVACATE) semi-dry FGD technology. With fly ash, $CaSO_3$, NaOH, Na_2SO_3 and other additives added into $Ca(OH)_2$ and then undergone a hydrated drying process, a highly active adsorbent can be prepared. In fixed beds or pipelines, both SO_2 and NO_x can be removed by injecting the aforementioned adsorbent at temperatures ranging from 60 – 125 °C. As the key point of this multi-pollutants removal technology, the preparation of this highly active absorbent necessitates a comprehensive consideration in the material share, additive types, hydration conditions, and other factors. The absorber surface properties, reaction temperature, gas humidity, ratio of NO_2 to SO_2, and O_2 content can all affect the multi-pollutants removal performance. These circumstances mean that this technology is not economic enough. Again, its general removal efficiency is not high enough, with a desulfurization efficiency usually reaching up to 80% and denitrification rate below 50% in lab-scale tests. For a called ADVACATE $deSO_x$ and $deNO_x$ technology, Rochelle' group [79,80] focused on the effects of different additives and reaction conditions on (i) the removal efficiencies and (ii) interaction between SO_2 and NO_x during the removal process, followed by establishing fixed-bed chemical reaction models to predict the $deSO_x$ and $deNO_x$ efficiencies. Sakai et al. [81] and Odowd et al. [82] also reported a number of related studies in this subject. On the basis of an increase of the specific surface area of a Ca-based sorbent, Jozewicz et al. [83] found that Hg^0, SO_2, and NO_x removal efficiencies could be enhanced by adding an oxidant into flue gas, thereby implementing successfully the collaborative removal of SO_2, NO_x, and Hg^0.

Na/Al_2O_3 adsorbent based multi-pollutants removal technology. The adsorbent used here is a sodium salt loaded on Al_2O_3, which can be further regenerated by CO, H_2, and other reductive gas. A NO_xSO technique belongs to this subject, with removal efficiencies of above 90% and 70% reported in SO_2 and NO_x panels, respectively [84].

NH_3/V_2O_x-TiO_2 adsorbent based multi-pollutants removal technology. The reactants of both desulfurization and denitrification are NH_3. It regards V_2O_x ($x = 4 - 5$), which is present on metal oxides such as TiO_2, as the catalyst. For example, Kasaoka et al. [85] employed this V_2O_x catalyst and NH_3 to conduct a series of SO_2/NO collaborative removal experiments at 130 °C in a fixed bed.

1.3.2.3 Free-Radical Based Multi-Pollutants Removal Technology

In this type, various high-energetic free radicals such as O, O_3, OH, and HO_2, which are generated by e-beam, pulsed-corona, and other plasma methods, are used to oxidize efficiently NO and Hg^0. Combined with a alkali absorption process and wet electrostatic precipitator, these free radicals can be used to effectively remove SO_2, NO_x, particles matter, heavy metals, and VOCs at the same time. Meanwhile, high-energetic free radicals can also generate N radical, which can reduce NO into N_2. But unfortunately, the energy consumption of this type is particularly high, since the triple bond N_2 is the most stable molecule in the flue gas environment. Generally, the free-radical based multi-pollutants removal technology includes e-beam and pulsed-corona methods.

E-beam method [86–92]. The research on e-beam simultaneous desulfurization and denitrification technologies began in the 20th century. In principle, all types of active groups (including OH, OH_2, O, and O_3), generated by the high-energy e-beam irradiation process of flue gas, can oxidize SO_2 and NO_x to generate H_2SO_4 and HNO_3, respectively. These acids react with the ejected NH_3 to form NH_4NO_3 and $(NH_4)_2SO_4$. Ebara Company in Japan has developed a commercial e-beam multi-pollutants removal technology, which uses a high-energy electron excitation of N_2, O_2, and H_2O molecules to generate N, O, O_3, OH, and other active radicals. With these free radicals assistance, NO and SO_2 can be oxidized to a high state naturally (i.e., the common forms of NO_2 and SO_3), which then react with NH_3 to generate by-products spontaneously. Ebara has applied this technology commercially in Chengdu and Hangzhou thermal power plants in China.

Pulsed-corona method [93,94]. The pulsed-corona method uses the pulsed-corona discharge to obtain active electrons. These active electrons are then injected into flue gas to break down molecular bonds of various components, so as to form a variety of active free radicals that used to remove SO_2 and NO_x. Khacef and Cormier [95] applied the pulsed-corona method to deal with SO_2 and NO_x in the flue gas of a glass processing plant. The Power Span Company adopts the corona discharging low-temperature plasma to remove NO_x, SO_2, PM, Hg, HCl, and other pollutants simultaneously, coupled with NH_3 absorption and wet electrostatic precipitators [96]. However, NH_3 can volatile easily and tends to have secondary pollution risk because of the NH_3 leakage.

1.3.2.4 Wet Chemical Multi-Pollutants Removal Technology

This type is characterized by the preparation of a solution coupled with special reagents. The solution is sprayed into flue gas to remove SO_2 and NO_x simultaneously. The drawbacks lie on a long time lasting for the gas component absorption process, low removal efficiency, and the potential secondary pollution because of the waste liquid discharge. Mainly divided by the added reagents, the wet chemical multi-pollutants removal technology has several subcategories.

Sub-ferrous complex method. Taking the sub-ferrous complex contained-SH groups as the absorbent, Shi *et al.* [97] used the renewable sub-ferrous cysteine solution to absorb SO_2 and NO_x and recycled sulfur to make the process easy. In another application example, Fe(EDTA) or some other denitrification absorbents such as sodium salts [98] was added into the wet desulfurization solution, so as to enhance the NO_x absorption.

Liquid-membrane method. The US Department of Energy developed an Fe(EDTA)-membrane method for simultaneous desulfurization and denitrification. Accordingly, a series of investigations into the simultaneous removal of SO_2 and NO_x by the solution-membrane method were performed in Steven Institute of Technology [99]. It was reported that in University of Calgary in Canada [100], flue-gas purification tests were conducted with polyethylene glycol and glycol amine as immobilized liquid membranes. Researchers in Nagoya University in Japan attended to investigate the removal of SO_2 and NO_x in flue gas with the help of Na or K carbonate, alkyl amines, and Na_2SO_3 aqueous solutions [101]. The absorption was based on the hydrophobic-microporous hollow-fiber membrane module liquid membrane method.

Strong oxidant method. As an effective co-removal approach for SO_2 and NO_x in flue gas, this technique type utilizes the strong oxidants (such as $NaClO_2/HClO_3$, $KMnO_4/NaOH$, P_4, and others [87–91]) that can oxidize NO and Hg^0 into theirs oxidized forms. The oxidized species, namely NO_2, $HgCl_2$, HgO, and etc are water-soluble to be easily removed in the WFGD process. However, these strong oxidants are of weakness spontaneously, such as corrosive and non-degradable, thereby irrefutably leading to a secondary pollution risk. As an example in this technique type, the NO_xSORB technology [102] developed in the Argonne National Laboratory, uses HClO and NaClO to oxidize NO to NO_2 and Hg^0 to Hg^{2+}. Subsequently, SO_2, NO_2, and Hg^{2+} can be successfully co-absorbed in the alkali solution. However, both chlorate and hypochlorite are strongly corrosive and un-degraded, which may have a secondary pollution risk.

References

[1]   Rubin ES, Hao Y. Engineering and Environment Introduction. Beijing: Science Press, 2004.

[2]   China Statistical Yearbook 1978–2007. National Bureau of Statistics of China. Beijing: Statistics Press, http://csp.stats.gov.cn.

[3]   Wang CH. Status of nitride oxide pollution and its treatment technology development and standards. Machniery Industry Standardization & Quality,

2008(3):20–22.

[4]   Bergan T, Gallardo L, Rodhe H. Atmosphere Environment, 1999(33):1575–1585.

[5]   Tang SB, Wang HC. Chemistry of Environmental Organic Pollution. Beijing: Metallurgical Industry Press, 1996.

[6]   Hu CX. The study of mercury discharge of coal-fired power plant and the stable adsorption mechanism of activated carbon. Ph.D thesis of Zhejiang University, 2007.

[7]   Communique of Environmental State of China in 2002–2007. Ministry of Environmental Protection of the People's Republic of China. http://jcs.mep. gov.cn/hjzl/zkgb/.

[8]   Pai D. Fluidized bed combustion technology: the past, present and future. Modem Power System, 1999(19):21–26.

[9]   Hao JM, Wang SX, Lu YQ. Manual of Coal-Fired Sulphur Dioxide Control Technology. Beijing: Chemical Industry Press, 2001.

[10] The Notice about Releasing the Policy of Coal-Fired Sulphur Dioxide Pollution Control Technology. Ministry of Environmental Protection of the People's Republic of China, 2002. http://www.sepa.gov.cn/eic/649086798147878912/ 20031008/1041859.html.

[11] Marika R, Ilari E. The flue gas desulfurization technology with high performance cost ratio. Electric Power Environmental Protective, 2001(17):8–10.

[12] Li LQ, Zeng GM. Development of the integrated equipment of dust removal and desulfurization of flue gas for coal-burning boiler. Techniques and Equipments for Environmental Pollution Control, 2000(1):39–43.

[13] Tai DR, Han BB. Industry demonstration project progress of flue gas desulfurization technology with electron beam. Environmental Science Advance, 1999(7):125–135.

[14] Yan YQ, Fan AX. Flue gas desulfurization technology and its solution selection principles. Sichuan Electric Power Technology, 2000(2):42–44.

[15] Dong XD, Peng SG. Flue-gas desulfurization with seawater and its application. China Power, 1996(10):52–57.

[16] Zhong Q. Coal-Fired Flue-Gas Desulfurization and Denitrification Technology and Case Studies. Beijing: Chemical Industry Press, 2002.

[17] Smoot LD, Hill SC, Xu H. NO_x control through reburning. Progress in Energy and Combustion Science, 1998(24):385–408.

[18] Xuan XP, Yao Y, Le CT, Li SY. Progress of the selective catalytic reduction of NO_x. Coal Conversion, 2002(25):26–31.

[19] Bosch H, Janssen F. Catalytic Reduction of Nitrogen Oxides: A Review on the Fundamentals and Technology. Elsevier Science Publishers, 1988.

[20] Chang MB, Cheng CF. Low temperature SNCR process for NO_x control. Science of the Total Environment, 1997(198):73–78.

[21] Wang ZH, Zhou H, Zhou JH, Fan JR, Cen KF. Modeling and experimental study

on NO_x reduction in furnace with ammonia injection. Journal of Fuel Chemistry and Technology, 2004(32):48–53.

[22] Zhong Q. NO_x removal with selective non-catalytic reduction. Journal of Nanjing University of Science and Technology, 2000(24):68–71.

[23] Kicherer A, Spliethoff H, Maier H, Hein KRG. The effect of different reburning fuels on NO_x-reduction. Fuel, 1994(73):1443–1446.

[24] Chen SL, Kramlich JC, Seeker WR, Pershing DW. Optimization of reburning for advanced NO_x control on coal-fired boilers. Journal of the Air & Waste Management Association, 1989(39):1375–1379.

[25] Hampartsoumian E, Folayan OO, Nimmo W, Gibbs BM. Optimisation of NO_x reduction in advanced coal reburning systems and the effect of coal type. Fuel, 2003(82):373–84.

[26] Liu H, Hampartsoumian E, Gibbs BM. Evaluation of the optimal fuel characteristics for efficient NO reduction by coal reburning. Fuel, 1997(76):985–993.

[27] Zamansky VM. Second Generation Advanced Reburning for high efficiency NO_x control. Energy and Environmental Research Corporation, DOE Report No. DE-AC22-95PC95251; 1997.

[28] Xiang J, Sun XX, Hu S, Yu DX. An experimental research on boiler combustion performance. Fuel Processing Technology, 2000(68):139–151.

[29] Tree DR, Clark AW. Advanced reburning measurements of temperature and species in a pulverized coal flame. Fuel, 2000(79):1687–1695.

[30] Bool L, Kobayashi H. NO_x reduction from a 44-MW wall-fired boiler utilizing oxygen enhanced combustion. Proceedings of the 28th International Technical Conference on Coal Utilization & Fuel Systems, Florida, USA, 2003.

[31] Cremer M, Wang H, Chen Z, Bool L, Thompson D, *et al*. CFD evaluation of oxygen enhanced combustion: impacts on NO_x emission, carbon-in-fly ash and waterwall corrosion. Proceedings of the 28th International Technical Conference on Coal Utilization & Fuel Systems, Florida, USA, 2003.

[32] Srivastava RK, Neuffer W, Grano D, Khan S, Staudt JE, Jozewicz W. Controlling NO_x emission from industrial sources. Environmental Progress, 2005(24):181–197.

[33] Chang R, Offen GR. Mercury emission control technologies: An EPRI synopsis. Power Engineering, 1995(51):51–57.

[34] Hu CX, Zhou JS, Luo ZY, He S, Wang GK, Cen KF. Effect of oxidation treatment on the adsorption and the stability of mercury on activated carbon. Journal of Environmental Sciences, 2006(18):1161–1166.

[35] Li JR, Maroto-Valer MM. Computational and experimental studies of mercury adsorption on unburned carbon present in fly ash. Carbon, 2012(50):1913–1924.

[36] Zhao Y, Liu S, Ma X, Yao J. Experimental investigation on mercury adsorption characteristics by modified Ca-based sorbent. Proceedings of the CSEE,

2009(29):50–54.

[37] Liu ST, Zhao Y, Wang LD, Zang ZY. Simultaneous removal of SO$_2$, NO and mercury by oxygen-enriched highly active absorbents. Journal of Power Engineering, 2008(28):420–424.

[38] Morency J. Zeolite sorbent that effectively removes mercury from flue gases. Filtration & Separation, 2002(39):24–26.

[39] Aeschliman D, Norton G. Collection and thermal evolution behaviors of different mercury species captured with gold. Environmental Science Technology, 1999(33):2278–2283.

[40] Mao JX, Mao JQ, Zhao SM. Clean Burning of Coal. Beijing: China Science Press, 2000.

[41] Meij R. The fate of mercury in coal-fired power plants and the influence of wet flue-gas desulphurization. Water, Air and Soil Pollution, 1991(56):21–33.

[42] Wu Y, Urabe T. Test study of eliminating mercury vapor through pulse discharge. Journal of Environmental Science, 1996(16):221–225.

[43] Ren JL, Zhou JX, Luo ZY, Cen KF. Investigation into mercury transformation mechanisms in laboratory combustion systems. International Conference on Energy and the Environment, Shanghai, China, 2003.

[44] Zhou JH, Luo ZY, Ren JL, Cen KF. Mercury transport during coal combustion and pyrolysis. Proceedings of the 26th International Technical Conference on Coal Utilization & Fuel Systems, Florida, USA, 2001.

[45] Wang NH. Test of new kind of semidry process for flue-gas desulfurization and its mechanism study. Ph.D thesis of Zhejiang University, 2001.

[46] Teng B. Test of semidry process for flue-gas desulfurization and its mechanism study. Ph.D thesis of Zhejiang University, 2004.

[47] Gao HL. Test of simulating the form change and removal of mercury in flue-gas and its mechanism research. Ph.D thesis of Zhejiang University, 2004.

[48] Atkinson R. Atmospheric chemistry of VOCs and NO$_x$. Atmospheric Environment, 2000(34):2063–2101.

[49] Chuang CL, Chiang PC, Chang EE. Modeling VOCs adsorption onto activated carbon. Chemosphere, 2003(53):17–27.

[50] Zhang WJ, Li HF, Yang CJ, Lai YH, Luo YC. Research on disposal organic waste gas by method of adsorption and catalytic combustion. Journal of Beijing Institute of Light Industry, 1997(15):89–98.

[51] Lv HC, Pan HM, Chen YX. Advances in the treatment of low concentration volatile organic compounds. Environmental Protection of Chemical Industry, 2001(21):324–327.

[52] Burgess JE, Parsons SA, Stuetz RM. Developments in odour control and waste gas treatment biotechnology: A review. Biotechnology Advances, 2001(19):35–63.

[53] Mills B. Review of methods of odor control. Filtration & Separation,

1995(32):147–152.

[54] Acuña ME, Pérez F, Auria R, Revah S. Microbiological and kinetic aspects of a bio filter for the removal of toluene from waste gases. Biotechnology and Bioengineering, 1999(63):175–184.

[55] Okazaki K, Ando T. NO_x reduction mechanism in coal combustion with recycled CO_2. Energy, 1997(22):207–215.

[56] Liu H, Katagiri S, Okazaki K. Drastic SO_x removal and influences of various factors in O_2/CO_2 pulverized coal combustion system. Energy & Fuels, 2001(15):403–412.

[57] Liu H, Katagiri S, Okazaki K. Decomposition behavior and mechanism of calcium sulfate under the condition of O_2/CO_2 pulverized coal combustion. Chemical Engineering Communications, 2001(187):199–214.

[58] Steward FR, Couturier M, Morris K. Firing coal and limestone in a low-NO_x burner to reduce SO_2 emissions. Journal of the Institute of Energy, 1992(65):177–184.

[59] Gullett BK, Bruce KR, Hansen WF, Hofmann JE. Sorbent/urea slurry injection for simultaneous SO_2/NO_x removal. Environmental Progress, 1992(11):155–162.

[60] Muzio LJ, Himes RM, Thompson RE. Simultaneous NO_x/SO_2 removal by the dry injection of lime-urea hydrate. No. DOE/PC/88860-T1. Fossil Energy Research Corp., Laguna Hills, CA (USA), 1990.

[61] Zhong Q. Experimental research of SO_2/NO removal with injecting dry sorbent. Chongqing Environmental Science, 1995(17):17–21.

[62] Lu SY. The formation, emission and control mechanism research of Dioxin during the burning of waste and coal. Ph.D thesis of Zhejiang University, 2004.

[63] Xiao HP. The mechanism research of desulfurization and denitrition with organic calcium. Ph.D thesis of Zhejiang University, 2006.

[64] Nimmo W, Patsias AA, Hampartsoumian E, Gibbs BM, Williams PT. Simultaneous reduction of NO_x and SO_2 emissions from coal combustion by calcium magnesium acetate. Fuel, 2004(83):149–155.

[65] Nimmo W, Patsias AA, Hampartsoumian E, Gibbs BM, Fairweather M, Williams PT. Calcium magnesium acetate and urea advanced reburning for NO control with simultaneous SO_2 reduction. Fuel, 2004(83):1143–1150.

[66] Atal A, Steciak J, Levendis YA. Combustion and SO_2-NO_x emissions of bituminous coal particles treated with calcium magnesium acetate. Fuel, 1995(74):495–506.

[67] Evans AP, Kudlac GA, Wolkinson JM, Chang R. SO_x-NO_x-RO_x-BO_x-high temperature baghouse performance. Proceedings of the 10th Particulate control symposium, Washington D.C., USA, 1993.

[68] Martinelli R, Doyle JB, Redinger KE, 1995. SO_x-NO_x-RO_x box technology review and global commercial opportunities. Proceedings of the 4th Annual Clean Coal Technology Conference, Denver, USA, 1995.

[69] Liu QY, Liu ZY. Honeycomb cordierite-based CuO/Al_2O_3 catalyst for simultaneous SO_2 and NO removal from flue gas. Journal of Fuel Chemistry and Technology, 2004(32):257–262.

[70] Bruno L, Ricci R. Application of SNO_x technology at the Gela power plant in Sicily. Proceedings of PowerGen 2000 Europe, Helsinki, Finland, 2000.

[71] Shemwell B, Atal A, Levendis YA, Simons GA. A laboratory investigation on combined in-furnace sorbent injection and hot flue-gas filtration to simultaneously capture SO_2, NO_x, HCl, and particulate emissions. Environmental Science & Technology, 2000(34):4855–4866.

[72] Schoubye P, Jensen FE. SNO_x^{TM} flue gas treatment for boilers burning petcoke makes petcoke more attractive for power and heat generation. Proceedings of the Petcoke Conference, Orlando, USA, 2007.

[73] Sverdrup GM, Riggs KB, Kelly TJ, Barrett RE, Peltier RG, Cooper JA. Toxic emissions from a cyclone burner boiler with an ESP and with the SNO_x demonstration and from a pulverized coal burner boiler with an ESP/wet flue gas desulfurization system. Proceedings of the Annual Meeting and Exhibition of the Air and Waste Management Association, Cincinnati, USA, 1994.

[74] Durrani SM. The SNO_x process: a success story. Environmental Science & Technology, 1994(28):88–90.

[75] Andeasen J, Laursen JK, Bendixen OR. SNO_x plant in full-scale operation. Modern Power Systems, 1992(12):57–60.

[76] Tsuji K, Shiraishi I. Combined desulfurization, denitrification and reduction of air toxics using activated coke: 1. Activity of activated coke. Fuel, 1997(76):549–553.

[77] Moberg G, Bild JO, Wallin S, Fareid T, Ralston J. Combined $DeNO_x/DeSO_x$ and additional NO_x reduction by cleaning flue gas condensate from ammonia. Proceedings of the PowerGen International Conference, New Orleans, USA, 1999.

[78] Haddad E, Ralston J, Green G, Castagnero S. Full-scale evaluation of a multi-pollutant reduction technology: SO_2, Hg and NO_x. Proceedings of the EPA-EPRI-NETL-AWMA Combined Power Plant Air Pollutant Control Mega Symposium, Washington D.C., USA, 2003.

[79] Chu P, Rochelle GT. Removal of SO_2 and NO_x from stack gas by reaction with calcium hydroxide solids. JAPCA, 1989(39):175–179.

[80] Nelli CH, Rochelle GT. Simultaneous sulfur dioxide and nitrogen dioxide removal by calcium hydroxide and calcium silicate solids. Journal of the Air & Waste Management Association, 1998(48):819–828.

[81] Sakai M, Su C, Sasaoka E. Simultaneous removal of SO_x and NO_x using slaked lime at low temperature. Industrial & Engineering Chemistry Research, 2002(41):5029–5033.

[82] O'Dowd WJ, Markussen JM, Pennline HW, Resnik KP. Characterization of NO_2

and SO_2 removals in a spray dryer/baghouse system. Industrial & Engineering Chemistry Research, 1994(33):2749–2756.

[83] Ghorishi SB, Singer CF, Jozewicz WS, Sedman, CB, Srivastava RK. Simultaneous control of Hg^0, SO_2, and NO_x by novel oxidized calcium-based sorbents. Journal of the Air & Waste Management Association, 2002(52):273–278.

[84] Ma WT, Chang M, Haslbeck JL, Neal LG. NO_xSO SO_2/NO_x flue gas treatment process adsorption chemistry and kinetics: novel adsorbents and their environmental applications. AIChE Symposium Series, 1995(91):309.

[85] Kasaoka S, Sasaoka E, Iwasaki H. Vanadium oxides (V_2O_x) catalysts for dry-type and simultaneous removal of sulfur oxides and nitrogen oxides with ammonia at low temperature. Bulletin of the Chemical Society of Japan, 1989(62):1226–1232.

[86] Kim H, Han J, Kawaguchi I, Minami W. Simultaneous removal of NO_x and SO_2 by a nonthermal plasma hybrid reactor. Energy & Fuels, 2007(21):141–144.

[87] Chmielewski AG, Dobrowolski A, Iller E. Development and application experience with technology of SO_2 and NO_x removal from flue gas by electron beam irradiation. Proceedings of the EPRI-DOE-EPA Combined Utility Air Pollution Control Symposium: the MEGA Symposium, Atlanta, USA, 1999.

[88] Maezawa A, Izutsu M. Application of e-beam treatment to flue gas cleanup in Japan. Non-Thermal Plasma Techniques for Pollution Control, 1993(34):47–54.

[89] Maezawa A, Iizuka Y. Electron beam flue gas treatment process technology. Proceedings of the International Congress of Acid Snow and Rain, Niigata, Japan, 1997.

[90] Chmielewski AG, Sun YX, Licki J, Bułka S, Kubica K, Zimek Z. NO_x and PAHs removal from industrial flue gas by using electron beam technology with alcohol addition. Radiation Physics and Chemistry, 2003(67):555–560.

[91] Namba H, Tokunaga O, Tanaka T, Ogura Y. The study of electron beam flue gas treatment for coal-fired thermal plant in Japan. Radiation Physics and Chemistry, 1993(42):669–672.

[92] Ighigeanu D, Martin D, Zissulescu E, Macarie R, Oproiu C, Cirstea E, *et al.* SO_2 and NO_x removal by electron beam and electrical discharge induced non-thermal plasmas. Vacuum, 2005(77):493–500.

[93] Dong LM, Lan S, Yang JX, Chi XC. Plasma chemical reaction for nitric oxide and sulfur dioxide removal in corona discharge reactor. Proceedings of Annual Report Conference on Electrical Insulation and Dielectric Phenomena, Albuquerque, USA, 2003.

[94] Hackam R, Akiyama H. Air pollution control by electrical discharges. IEEE Transactions on Dielectrics and Electrical Insulation, 2000(7):654–683.

[95] Khacef A, Cormier JM. Pulsed sub-microsecond dielectric barrier discharge treatment of simulated glass manufacturing industry flue gas: removal of SO_2 and

NO_x. Journal of Physics D-Applied Physics, 2006(39):1078–1083.

[96] McLarnon CR, Steen D. Combined SO_2, NO_x, PM, and Hg removal from coal fired boilers. Proceedings of the Mega Symposium, Washington D.C., USA, 2003.

[97] Shi Y, Wang H, Chang SG. Kinetics of NO absorption in aqueous iron (II) thiochelate solutions. Environmental Progress, 1997(16):301–306.

[98] Shen CH, Rochelle GT. Nitrogen dioxide absorption and sulfite oxidation in aqueous sulfite. Environmental Science & Technology, 1998(32):1994–2003.

[99] Okamoto M. SO_2 separation by liquid reactive membranes. Separation Technology, 1994(11):755–802.

[100] Kobayashi H, Takezawa N, Niki T. Removal of Nitrogen-Oxides with Aqueous-Solutions of Inorganic and Organic-Reagents. Environmental Science & Technology, 1977(11):190–192.

[101] Joshi JB, Mahajani VV, Juvekar VA. Invited review absorption of NO_x gases. Chemical Engineering Communications, 1985(33):1–92.

[102] Livengood CD, Mendelssohn MH. Process for combined control of mercury and nitric oxide. EPRI-DOE-EPA Combined Utility Air Pollutant Control Symposium, Georgia, Atlanta, 1999.

2

Principle of Multi-Pollutants Removal Technology in Flue Gas by Ozone

2.1 Introduction

NO_x, which are a significant threat to the environment, usually consist of 95% NO in coal-fired flue gas. NO is characteristic of an extremely low water-solubility. Thus, a process similar to that used to remove sulfur content from flue gas is barely applicable for NO_x removal. On the contrary, compounds with a high N valence (i.e., NO_2, NO_3, and N_2O_5) have a high solubility in water to produce HNO_3. This means that when initially oxidizing to these compounds and then using an alkaline solution process, NO can be removed together with other acid gases (such as SO_2, HCl, and HF) in flue gas [1]. Similarly, 80% – 90% of Hg^{2+} (i.e., HgO, $HgCl_2$, and Hg_2Cl_2) can be eliminated by WFGD even though Hg is hardly soluble in water [2,3]. Table 2.1 shows the water solubilities of main pollutants in flue gas.

Due to the oxidized compounds with higher solubilities, all of NO, SO_2 and Hg attend to be initially oxidized into the oxidized species by ozone and then eliminated successfully by an alkaline solution integrated with WFGD. As a result, a technology characterized by the simultaneous removal of SO_2, NO, Hg, HCl, and VOCs in flue gas by ozone oxidation, has been examined to be applicable in both bench-scale and pilot test facilities.

Fig. 2.1 presents the typical multi-pollution control technology that utilizes ozone. This system consists of the following main steps:

1) Oxygen production. Oxygen is produced in an air separation unit.

2) Ozone generation. The ozone generation technology has been

developed in Europe for more than 30 years.

3)   Scrubber. Ozone is injected into the tube by instruments similar to those employed in selective catalytic reduction systems.

4)   Wet removal unit. In this unit, $Ca(NO_3)_2$ is produced from the FGD system that uses Ca.

Table 2.1   Water solubilities of main pollutants in flue gas (g/100 g water)

Species	0 °C	20 °C	40 °C	60 °C	80 °C	100 °C
NO	0.00984	0.00618	0.00440	0.00324	0.00199	0
NO_2	High	High	High	High	High	High
SO_2	22.83	11.29	5.41			
SO_3	High	High	High	High	High	High
Hg	Null	Null	Null	Null	Null	Null
HgO		$5.2×10^{-3}$	Dissolvable in acid and alkaline			
$HgCl_2$	3.6	6.5	10.2	16.2	30.0	61.3
Hg_2Cl_2	0.00014	0.00020	0.00070			

Note: <0.01, null; 0.01–1, slightly soluble; 1–10, soluble; >10, highly soluble

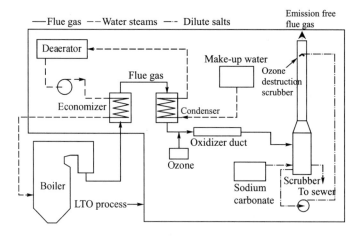

Fig. 2.1   Diagram of a typical multi-pollution control technology using ozone

The following methods can be applied to eliminate the nitrates produced from the system:

· $Ca(NO_3)_2$ and CaCl can be processed in available ash pits and landfills.

· $Ca(NO_3)_2$ and CaCl can be processed in wastewater treatment.

· $Ca(NO_3)_2$ and CaCl can be processed by using metals to produce fertilizers.

· Enriched Ca(NO₃)₂ can be recycled and sold as by-product.

· Combined with lime, nitrates can be used as construction materials.

This technology can also co-produce the ammonia sulfate fertilizer by using the FGD system that re-utilizes ammonia. In addition, solutions such as NaS/NaOH can also be used to absorb the pollutants.

Ozone oxidation mechanisms are explained possibly as below. Analytically, both the oxidation of SO_2 and CO seem not as quick as the NO_x reaction.

$$O_3+NO=NO_2+O_2 \tag{2.1}$$
$$O_3+2NO_2=N_2O_5+O_2 \tag{2.2}$$
$$CO+O_3=CO_2+O_2 \tag{2.3}$$
$$SO_2+O_3=SO_3+O_2 \tag{2.4}$$
$$O_3+Hg=HgO+O_2 \tag{2.5}$$

2.2 Ozone Characteristics

In general, each ozone molecule with the potential molecular structures presented in Fig. 2.2, comprises three oxygen atoms. Ozone is chemically active and has a pungent odor. 85% − 90% of the total available natural ozone is located in the stratosphere. The 10 − 45 km space surrounding the Earth is occupied by ozone and thus called the ozonesphere. Ozone in the stratosphere protects the Earth by absorbing the ultraviolet radiation. However, harmful ozone can be produced through the photochemical reactions of VOCs and NO_x with sunshine [4].

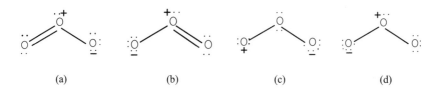

| (a) | (b) | (c) | (d) |

Fig. 2.2 Typical structures of the ozone resonance hybrid molecule

As a blue gas with density of 2.144 kg/m³ at standard state, ozone melts at −192.5 °C and boils at −111.9 °C. At standard state, its water solubility is 13 times higher than that of oxygen and 25 times higher than that of air. Ozone automatically decomposes into oxygen so that it is not stable enough in the air. Again, ozone is explosive when its concentration exceeds 25% because of the massive heat produced from decomposition. Fortunately, its concentration in air is usually less than 10% [5]. Ozone is a strong oxide and has an electrode potential of 2.07 V. With the electrode potentials of several strong oxides listed in Table 2.2, it can be seen that only F_2 with a potential of 2.78 V exceeds that of ozone. Ozone can react with organic matters in three ways of (i) normal chemical reactions, (ii) peroxide production, and (iii) decomposition. For example, the reaction of ozone with toxic xylene produces non-toxic carbon dioxide and water. The interaction of ozone with polar organic substances causes breakage of the double bonds [6].

Table 2.2 Electrode potentials of common oxides

Name	Formula	Standard electrode potentials (V)
Fluorine	F_2	2.87
Ozone	O_3	2.07
Peroxide	H_2O_2	1.78
Potassium permanganate	MnO_4^-	1.67
Chloride dioxide	ClO_2	1.50
Chlorine	Cl_2	1.36
Oxygen	O_2	1.23

Given its strong oxidizing property, ozone can be utilized in environmental engineering to sterilize water and to eliminate water contaminants. Oxygen is the only residue of ozone decomposition. Thus, oxygen is widely used in hospital and water treatment [7–10]. However, the unsteady chemical composition of ozone brings challenges to its storage and transportation.

2.3   Ozone Generation Methods

Jet bombardment, such as electron, nuclear, plasma, and ultraviolet radiation, decomposes oxygen into oxygen atom. This type of oxygen atom combines with oxygen molecule to form the triatomic ozone. Stratospheric ozone may be created by the UV radiation action. The detailed process involving the creation of stratospheric ozone is given as follows:

$$O_2+h\upsilon=O+O \tag{2.6}$$
$$O+O_2=O_3 \tag{2.7}$$
$$O_3+h\upsilon=O_2+O \tag{2.8}$$
$$O+O_3=2O_2 \tag{2.9}$$

Several methods could be employed to generate ozone, including corona discharge, nuclear radiation, UV radiation, electrolysis, and so on. The industrial ozone production is mainly facilitated by plasma discharge. In this method, ozone is generally generated through the passage of oxygen (or air) across the plasma discharging zone. The fundamental principle in the ozone synthesis through plasma discharge involves placing the oxygen-containing gas in a discharging reactor, which is characterized by a low-temperature plasma atmosphere. Free electrons at a certain energy level break oxygen molecules into oxygen atoms. Ozone molecules are then produced through the three-body collision reaction, while the ozone decomposition reaction occurs at the same time. Under the plasma discharging conditions, ozone is generally believed to be obtained through the following ways:

$$O_2+e=O+O+e \qquad\qquad (2.10)$$
$$O+O_2+M=O_3+M \qquad\qquad (2.11)$$
$$O+O_3=2O_2 \qquad\qquad (2.12)$$
$$e+O_3=O+O_2+e \qquad\qquad (2.13)$$

Two oxygen atoms are produced by using high-energy electron bombarding. Oxygen atoms and oxygen molecules form O_3 through three-body collision reaction, where M is a third-party gas molecule. Meanwhile, the O atom accompanied with electrons may re-decompose O_3. The ozone concentration at the generator outlet is determined by a balance between the ozone generation and destruction within the corona area. Various factors can affect the ozone yield, such as the oxygen content in the feed gas, temperature, air purity, corona power density, electrode cooling efficiency. For example, under same conditions, the ozone output generated from pure oxygen is approximately two times of that from air. Dust, oil, organic matters, and other impurities in the air source can affect the electric current movement and adhere to the electrode surface, thereby influencing the ozone production. Again, excessive vapor in the air source develops an arc discharge to waste energy. Therefore, the air dew point is controlled at temperatures ranging from −50 °C to −40 °C. Most of the power input within the corona is dissipated in the form of heat, whereas a small part of the power input is converted into light, sound, and chemical energies. Improving the frequency and voltage of the power source is beneficial to the ozone production. However, manufacturing the power source is difficult, and the dielectric parts of the power source are easily broken [5].

Nowadays, low-temperature plasma, which is obtained under room temperature, is used to produce ozone. Different discharge types correspond to different functions, including corona discharge, silent discharge, surface discharge, pulse corona/streamer discharge, mixed discharge, and glow discharge. In recent years, numerous theoretical studies, technological improvements, and new attempts have been conducted to improve the ozone generation efficiency. Most of them give prominence to the following aspects.

2.3.1 *Electrode Type*

Investigations into various electrodes (including linear, brush-like, spiral, mesh, rotating, and water electrodes) has been performed so as to improve the discharge condition and efficiency. Fig. 2.3 presents various electrode forms [11,12].

Gibalov and Pietsch [13,14] theoretically and experimentally analyzed the electric field, neutral particles, charged particles, and energy density distribution of the coplanar dielectric barrier discharge (DBD) (Fig. 2.4) in correlation to space and time. It was found that the electric field intensity ranged from 70 – 100 TD when the gas source was air or pure oxygen. Boonseng *et al.* [15] developed a new ozone generator with a brush-like electrode (the structure shown in Fig. 2.5) for water treatment. Because the brush-like electrode increased the ionization area and power, a strong non-uniform electric field thus developed and the ozone generation efficiency increased. It was found that under circumstances with the voltage and frequency of 15 kV and 20 kHz, the ozone concentration reached 64 ppm and ozone production efficiency exceeded 716 mg/(kW·h). Within a tube-type reactor (Fig. 2.6), Yehia's group [16–18] focused on comparing the ozone production with respect to the electrode structure (including the wire-pipe, wire-rectangular, and coaxial-tube types). Given the same wire diameter, discharge power, and flow rate, a wire-tube-type electrode structure results in a larger discharge current and higher ozone concentration, compared with a wire-rectangular type, regardless of the alternating current (AC) or direct current (DC) power source used. Among the three electrode structures, the coaxial-tube type with silent discharging results in the highest ozone concentration, regardless of the size of the wire and width of the gap used.

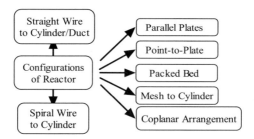

Fig. 2.3   Types of electrode [11,12] (With permission from High Voltage Technique)

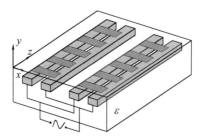

Fig. 2.4   Schematic of the coplanar reactor [13,14] (With permission from Journal of Physics D-Applied Physics)

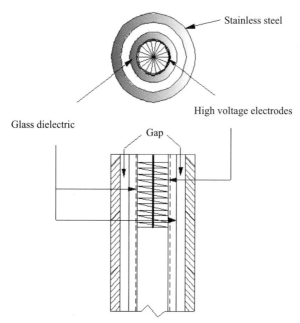

Fig. 2.5   Schematic of the bush-like electrode [15]

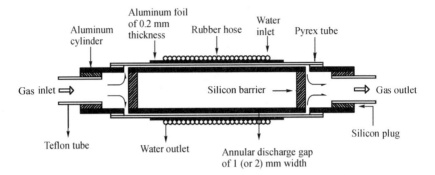

Fig. 2.6 Schematic of the tube-type reactor [16–18] (With permission from Journal of Physics D-Applied Physics)

2.3.2 Feed Gas

Organic matter [19–22]: Organic matters react with oxygen atoms when hydrocarbons and halogenated hydrocarbons are added. These reactions consume oxygen atoms and reduce the ozone production. When the hydrocarbon content is greater than 1%, no ozone is produced.

Oxygen-contained compound [23–25]: More $O(^1D)$ radicals are consumed with increasing N_2O; this behavior significantly decreases the ozone production. When the gas mixture contains 70% N_2O, the generated ozone concentration is less than 2 ppm. The formation of $O^- \cdot (N_2O)_n$ and $NO^- \cdot (N_2O)_n$ results in a small discharge current. With regard to CO_2 and H_2O, the ozone yield increases with increasing O_2 concentration.

Non-oxygen-contained compound [26–28]: Under the circumstance with the SF_6 concentration range 0.08% – 0.8%, the ozone concentration increases with increasing SF_6. Novoselov *et al.* [27] assumed that the highest ozone concentration would be obtained when N_2 concentration was within 20% – 30%, whereas Skalny *et al.* [26] believed that the ozone concentration decreased with increasing N_2. However, it should be noted that the energy input density was different in their experiments [26,27]. For Ar and H_2, the ozone concentration increased with increasing O_2. Skalny *et al.* [28] discovered that when the O_2 content was less than 20%, adding N_2 into the mixture attained a better ozone production performance, compared with adding Ar.

2.3.3   Dielectric Material

The dielectric, which is an important part of a silent electrical discharge system (i.e., the dielectric barrier discharge) equipped in an ozone generator, is used to strengthen the electric-field intensity in air gap for a more successful discharge. In addition, the dielectric prevents the air gap from breakdown, reduces power consumption, develops a uniform electric field in the air gap, and expands the discharge area, thereby facilitating the ozone generation. Generally, a higher dielectric constant corresponds to a better thermal conductivity and thus promotes the ozone production.

Currently, the dielectric in an ozone generator can be made by quartz glass, ceramic, enamel, and various types of organic materials. These materials are described below.

1) Ceramic and enamel

Highly pure alumina ceramics are characterized by a high melting point, mechanical strength, breakdown voltage, resistance to chemical corrosion, and thermal conductivity. In recent years, the material and processing technique applied in dielectric layers have become the key technologies in forming a strongly-ionized dielectric barrier discharge field. Through the plasma spraying or other methods, an ultrathin and dense α-Al_2O_3 dielectric layer is formed in the surface (with an area of 400 – 1600 cm^2) of both the discharge and grounding electrodes. Consequently, various advantages such as high strength, high density, high insulation, high dielectric constant, high uniformity, low curvature correction, and low loss appear in this type of dielectric layers [29–31].

Aside from theirs high electric strength, large dielectric constant, and strong corrosion resistance, ceramics also have a simple manufacturing process [32].

2) Bi-dielectric composite materials

In this aspect, only the mica application is selected as the example. Zhao *et al.*[33] used a ferroelectric/dielectric gap structure comprising a pair of plate electrodes and dual dielectric layers. A 0.1-mm-thick mica layer was positioned on the lower electrode. Meanwhile, a 1-mm-thick teflon layer with several centrally-located 10-mm-i.d. holes (used to position 1-mm-i.d. – 3-mm-i.d. ferroelectric spheres), was located on the mica layer. This mica and teflon bi-dielectric configuration can extend the ozone generator duration under high-humidity conditions.

3) Organic polymer material

Wang *et al.* [34] introduced a dielectric tube with an internal diameter of 69 mm and thickness of 12 mm, which was made by a kind of organic-polymer plastic with excellent properties (including a long duration at 145 °C, strong electrical insulation, extensibility, size stability, chemical corrosion resistance, self-extinguishing and flame-retardant abilities, non-toxicity, and so on). Zhu *et al.*[35] suggested that with glass replaced by polycarbonate in the dielectric and using the air source, both the ozone production rate and mass concentration in each dielectric tube could reach relatively high levels, in addition to low power consumption and economical operation. With maintaining the operational voltage below 6370 V and simultaneously increasing the discharge frequency, the ozone-generating tube degradation process postponed, developing a trouble-free service lifespan exceeding 8000 h.

4) Glass

With the development of the glass material and sintering technology, in the recent years glass has been used as the dielectric material in many ozone generators.

2.3.4 *Mixed Discharges*

A number of improvements in increasing the ozone production efficiency have been achieved by combining two types of discharges. These combined patterns include surface and silent discharges, surface and corona discharges, glow and silent discharges [36–40].

Nomoto *et al.* [41] generated ozone by using a combination of silent and surface discharges. It was found that using a mixed gas source (i.e., 80% N_2 + 20% O_2), the ozone yield reached 110 g/(kW·h) and was approximately two times of that only with silent discharge. Moreover, when using oxygen as the gas source, the combined discharge pattern generated a maximal ozone yield up to 274 g/(kW·h), equaling to approximately 2.5 times of that only with silent discharge.

Ma and Qiu [42] designed a silent-surface hybrid discharge ozone generator by using solenoid and metal electrodes. Experimental results showed that with pure oxygen as the gas source, the ozone yield rate achieved 295 g/(kW·h) when the output ozone concentration was relatively high at 1.3 mg/L. In 1999, Hakiai *et al.*[43] reported the ozone generation and distribution characteristics in an ozone generator equipped with a combination of the glow discharge and silent discharges. In 2003, Ahn *et al.* [44] reported the ozone generation characteristics by duplicating the surface and corona discharges. Their results had a maximum ozone yield of 247 g/(kW·h), which is two times that with a single discharge.

Song *et al.* [45] conducted multi-discharge experiments in an ozone generator with two discharge spaces and three electrode structures, as shown in Fig. 2.7(a). In these experiments, the central electrode was grounded. With a 180° phase difference, two high AC voltages were imposed on the inner and outer electrodes, respectively. Consequently, the ozone concentration and production rate reached as high as 17185 ppm and 783 g/(kW·h), respectively. In light of the arc discharge limitations in the discharge power and size, Shimosaki *et al.* [46] and Kaneda *et al.* [47] studied effects of the dielectric material and trigger electrode configuration (Fig. 2.7(b)) on the ozone yield assisted by mixed discharges. Results showed that covering partly the dielectrics could increase the ozone concentration and production rate. A maximum ozone production rate of 115 g/(kW·h) appeared under the circumstances with four trigger electrodes used.

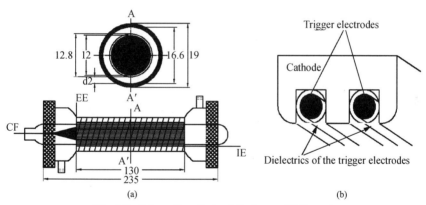

Fig. 2.7 Schematics of mixed discharges (Unit: mm)

2.3.5 Pulsed Discharge

Among various discharge types, pulsed discharge is very favorable for plasma chemical reactions. This discharge type has been widely used in the desulfurization and denitrification fields and has already achieved good performance. A nanosecond pulse can generate a pulse power, whose pulsed discharge can be used to efficiently produce ozone. Advantages of pulsed discharge in generating ozone are summarized as follows: (i) Less energy is needed when transforming a gas source into ions and neutral substances. A sophisticated cooling system that used to cool electrodes is no longer needed in the cooling system, thereby reducing the cost; (ii) High energy electrons are produced; (iii) The dielectric existence eliminates the spread of charged particles, resulting in the streamer evenly distributing on the dielectric surface; (iv) The dielectric existence can also eliminate the emission of cathode electrons and inhibit the occurrence of an arc discharge phenomenon, thereby promoting the streamer discharge. The published experimental results [48–52] have indicated that the aforementioned ozone generator system equipped with pulsed discharge is promising. However, before the real application, a number of issues need to be resolved, such as (i) the lifespan and cost of the high-voltage power that used to generate the nanosecond pulse and (ii) applicable methods for increasing the discharge power.

Samaranayake *et al.* [53,54] experimentally studied the ozone generation by using streamer discharge. It was found that the in a dry-air atmosphere and without dielectric material, the ozone concentration increased with the energy input density, whereas under the circumstances with PVC as the dielectric, this concentration initially increased but then decreased. With the pulse repetition frequency, air gap, and gas flow rate of 25 pps, 11 mm, and 3.0 L/min, respectively, the ozone production rate attained the maximum value of 202 g/(kW·h). For a spiral-cylindrical pulsed discharge electrode without dielectric material, results from Namihira's group [55–57] suggested with the pulse repetition frequency below 500 pps, pulse width of 130 ns, and oxygen as the gas source, the ozone production rate achieved 100 g/(kW·h), accompanied by the ozone concentration of 30 g/m^3. Also in the field of pulsed discharge used for ozone generation, Shimomura *et al.* [58] experimentally obtained the highest ozone production rate of 350 g/(kW·h), while Samaranayake *et al.* [59,60] numerically investigated the ozone generation assisted by the pulsed discharge method.

Understanding well the streamer propagation mechanism facilitates to improve the ozone production efficiency of the pulsed discharge. Accordingly, Tsukamoto *et al.* [57] experimentally obtained a streamer propagation velocity of 4.7×10^7 cm/s, whereas Namihira *et al.* [56] acquired a clearly higher measurement of $1.8 \times 10^8 -$ 3.3×10^8 cm/s. Although the two mentioned levels are different from those reported values (i.e., 1.1×10^6, 4.4×10^7, 9×10^7, and 1.8×10^8 cm/s), it can be determined that the streamer propagation velocity under different experimental conditions should range from 10^6 to 10^8 cm/s. Ono and Oda [61,62] conducted further research on the formation and structure of the primary and secondary streamers in the pulse corona discharge system, as well as the spatial distribution of ozone density. For a multi-point-offset structure with a pulse width of 100 μs and gas gap of 13 mm, it was found that the ozone density stopped increasing after 100 μs since the pulse discharge operation. The reaction rate of $O+O_2+M=O_3+M$ was $3.5×10^{-34}$ cm^6/s. Experimental results uncovered that ozone mainly appeared in the secondary streamer channel; this observation suggests that before ozone spreading to the other zones, most of ozone is generated by the secondary streamer. Moreover, the ozone diffusion coefficient was calculated to be $0.1 - 0.2$ cm^2/s.

2.4 Summary

This chapter provides a brief introduction on the principle of simultaneous removal of multi-pollutants using ozone. In addition, the physical and chemical properties of ozone are summarized. Ozone generation methods and a summary review of ozone generated technologies with discharge plasma are also provided.

References

[1] Thomas D, Vanderschuren J. Nitrogen oxides scrubbing with alkaline solutions. Chemical Engineering & Technology, 2000(23):449–455.

[2] Pavlish JH, Sondreal EA, Mann MD, Olson ES, Galbreath KC, Laudal DL, *et al.* State review of mercury control options for coal-fired power plants. Fuel Processing Technology, 2003(82):89–165.

[3] Martin K, Gonzalez E, Zhou CQ, Livengood CD. Elemental mercury removal using a wet scrubber. Proceedings of the American Power Conference, Chicago, USA, 1999.

[4] Rubin ES, Hao Y. Engineering and Environment Introduction. Beijing: Science Press, 2004.

[5] Chu J, Wu C, Chen W, Chen Z. Ozone Technology and Application. Beijing: Chemical Industry Press, 2002.

[6] Li L, Zhu W, Li H. Removal of refractory pollutants with catalytic ozonation adsorption technology. China Water & Wastewater, 2002(18):23–25.

[7] Chen M. Ozone technology and its application investigation in water treatment.

Mechanical & Electronical Equipment, 2002(4):28–31.

[8]   Liu C. Research development of ozone advanced oxidation technology in water treatment. Petrochemical Technology and Application, 2002(20):278–280.

[9]   Sun D, Yu X, Feng Y. Advanced Oxidation Technology in Environmental Engineering. Beijing: Chemical Industry Press, 2002.

[10] NIST. Chemical Kinetics Database on the Web. http://kinetics.nist.gov/index.php.

[11] Mitsuo T, Ritsuo A, Tomoihiro D. Electric discharge type ozone generator with point contact anode. JP,191907,20032012081.

[12] Yue C, Chen W, Chu J. Corona discharge ozone generator electrode research. High Voltage Technique, 2002(28):42–44.

[13] Gibalov VI, Pietsch GJ. Properties of dielectric barrier discharges in extended coplanar electrode systems. Journal of Physics D-Applied Physics, 2004(37):2093–2100.

[14] Gibalov VI, Pietsch GJ. Dynamics of dielectric barrier discharges in coplanar arrangements. Journal of Physics D-Applied Physics, 2004(37):2082–2092.

[15] Boonseng C, Kinnares V, Apriratikul P. Harmonic analysis of corona discharge ozone generator using brush electrode configuration. Proceedings of IEEE Power Engineering Society Winter Meeting, Singapore, 2000.

[16] Abdel-Salam M, Hashem A, Yehia A, Mizuno A, Turky A, Gabr A. Characteristics of corona and silent discharges as influenced by geometry of the discharge reactor. Journal of Physics D-Applied Physics, 2003(36):252–260.

[17] Yehia A, Abdel-Salam M, Mizuno A. On assessment of ozone generation in dc coronas. Journal of Physics D-Applied Physics, 2000(33):831–835.

[18] Yehia A, Mizuno A, Takashima K. On the characteristics of the corona discharge in a wire-duct reactor. Journal of Physics D-Applied Physics, 2000(33):2807–2814.

[19] Akhmedzhanov RA, Vikharev AL, Gorbachev AM, Ivanov OA, Kolysko AL. The role of atomic oxygen $O(^3P)$ in decomposition of freon in a nanosecond corona discharge. Technical Physics Letters, 1996(22):104–106.

[20] Cicman P, Pavlik M, Rahel J. Negative corona discharge in air+CCl_2F_2 mixture. Proceedings of Contributed Papers ICPIG 97, Toulouse, France, 1997.

[21] Skalny JD, Mason NJ. The effect of halomethane impurities on ozone generation from oxygen in DC negative corona discharge. Ozone-Science & Engineering, 2002(24):329–341.

[22] Skalny JD, Rahel J, Holubcik L. Ozone generation in oxygen-fed wire-to-cylinder ozonizer: Effect of CH_2Cl_2, $CHCl_3$ and CCl_4 diluents. Czechoslovak Journal of Physics 1999(49):335–348.

[23] Mikoviny T, Kocan M, Matejcik S, Mason NJ, Skalny JD. Experimental study of negative corona discharge in pure carbon dioxide and its mixtures with oxygen. Journal of Physics D-Applied Physics, 2004(37):64–73.

[24] Skalny JD, Matejcik S, Mikoviny T, Eden S, Mason NJ. Ozone generation in a negative corona discharge fed with N_2O and O_2. Journal of Physics D-Applied Physics, 2004(37):1052–1057.

[25] Stefanovic I, Bibinov NK, Deryugin AA, Vinogradov IP, Napartovich AP, Wiesemann K. Kinetics of ozone and nitric oxides in dielectric barrier discharges in O_2/NO_x and $N_2/O_2/NO_x$ mixtures. Plasma Sources Science & Technology, 2001(10):406–416.

[26] Skalny JD, Mikoviny T, Mason NJ. Experimental investigations and modeling studies of ozone producing corona discharges. Czechoslovak Journal of Physics, 2002(23):29–37.

[27] Novoselov YN, Ryzhov VV, Suslov AI. Effect of electronegative impurities on the generation of ozone in air. Technical Physics, 1999(44):44–47.

[28] Skalny JD, Mikoviny T, Mason NJ, Sobek V. The effect of gaseous diluents on ozone generation from oxygen. Ozone-Science & Engineering, 2002(24):29–37.

[29] Chu J, Wu C, Chen W. Ozone Technology and Application. Beijing: Chemical Industry Press, 2002.

[30] Liu W, Wu J, Chen Y. Ozone generator modification with Al_2O_3 ceramic substrates. Ceramic Technology, 2001(22):175–179.

[31] Zhang Z, Bai M. High concentration ozone generator discharge experimental study. High Voltage Technique, 2003(29):33–35.

[32] Park SL, Moon JD, Lee SH, Shin SY. Effective ozone generation utilizing a meshed-plate electrode in a dielectric-barrier discharge type ozone generator. Journal of Electrostatics, 2006(64):275–282.

[33] Zhao C, He Z, Li J. Research advances of gas discharge ozone generator. High Voltage Technique, 2002(28):44–46.

[34] Wang F, Zhu T, Yao H. Design of ozone generating pipe and its stability research. Hehai University Changzhou Campus Journal, 2002(16):1–5.

[35] Zhu T, Zhou H, Bian X. Research of organic polymer dielectric body ozone generating pipe properties. High Voltage Technique, 2002(28):38–40.

[36] Kishida H, Ishizaka M, Tanaka Y, Ehara Y, Ito T. Superposed effect of UV rays on ozone generation by electrical discharge. Electrical Engineering in Japan, 1998(123):8–14.

[37] Kishida H, Tamura M, Ehara Y, Ito T, Onouchi H. Improvement in ozone yield using discharge superposition method. Electrical Engineering in Japan, 1999(126):1–6.

[38] Hakiai K, Ihara S, Satoh S, Yamabe C. Characteristics of ozone generation by a diffuse glow discharge at atmospheric pressure using a double discharge method. Electrical Engineering in Japan, 1999(127):8–14.

[39] Masuda S, Koizumi S, Inoue J, Araki H. Production of ozone by surface and glow-discharge at cryogenic temperatures. IEEE Transactions on Industry Applications, 1988(24):928–933.

[40] Nomura T, Ehara Y, Ito T, Matsuyama M. Effect of applied voltage frequency on NO_x removal rate for a superimposing discharge reactor. Journal of Electrostatics, 2000(49):83–93.

[41] Nomoto Y, Ohkubo T, Kanazawa S, Adachi T. Improvement of ozone yield by a silent-surface hybrid discharge ozonizer. IEEE Transactions on Industry Applications, 1995(31):1458–1462.

[42] Ma HB, Qiu YC. A study of ozone synthesis in coaxial cylinder pulse streamer corona discharge reactors. Ozone-Science & Engineering, 2003(25):127–135.

[43] Hakiai K, Takazaki D, Ihara S, Satoh S, Yamabe C. Spatial distribution and characteristics of ozone generation with glow discharge using a double discharge method. Japanese Journal of Applied Physics Part 1—Regular Papers Short Notes & Review Papers, 1999(38):221–224.

[44] Ahn HS, Hayashi N, Ihara S, Yamabe C. Ozone generation characteristics by superimposed discharge in oxygen-fed ozonizer. Japanese Journal of Applied Physics Part 1—Regular Papers Short Notes & Review Papers, 2003(42):6578–6583.

[45] Song HJ, Chun BJ, Lee KS. Improvement of ozone yield by a multi-discharge type ozonizer using superposition of silent discharge plasma. Journal of the Korean Physical Society, 2004(44):1182–1188.

[46] Shimosaki M, Hayashi N, Ihara S, Satoh S, Yamabe C. Effect of trigger electrodes configuration of a double discharge ozonizer on ozone generation characteristics. Vacuum, 2004(73):573–577.

[47] Kaneda S, Hayashi N, Ihara S, Satoh S, Yamabe C. Application of dielectric material to double-discharge-type ozonizer. Vacuum, 2004(73):567–571.

[48] Buntat Z, Harry JE, Smith IR. Application of dimensional analysis to ozone production by pulsed streamer discharge in oxygen. Journal of Physics D-Applied Physics, 2003(36):1553–1557.

[49] Chalmers ID, Zanella L, MacGregor SJ. Ozone synthesis in oxygen in a dielectric barrier free configuration. Pulsed Power Conference, Albuquerque, USA, 1995.

[50] Akiyama H, Nishihashi Y, Tsukamoto S. Streamer discharge by pulsed power on a spiral transmission line. Pulsed Power Conference, Baltimore, USA, 1997.

[51] Simek M, Clupek M. Efficiency of ozone production by pulsed positive corona discharge in synthetic air. Journal of Physics D-Applied Physics, 2002(35):1171–1175.

[52] Motret O, Hibert C, Pouvesle JM. Ozone production by an ultra-short triggered dielectric barrier discharge. Geometrical considerations. Ozone: Science & Engineering, 2002(24):203–213.

[53] Samaranayake WJM, Hackam R, Akiyama H. Ozone synthesis in a cylindrical dry air-fed ozonizer by non thermal gas discharges. Proceedings of the 7th International Conference on Properties and Applications of Dielectric Materials,

Nagoya, Japan, 2003.

[54] Samaranayake WJM, Namihira T, Katsuki S, Miyahara Y, Sakugawa T, Hackam R, *et al*. Pulsed power production of ozone using nonthermal gas discharges. IEEE Electrical Insulation Magazine, 2001(17):17–25.

[55] Namihira T, Shinozaki K, Katsuki S, Hackam R, Akiyama H, Sakugawa T. Characteristics of ozonizer using pulsed power. Proceedings of Pulsed Power Plasma Science, Las Vegas, USA, 2001.

[56] Namihira T, Wang DY, Katsuki S, Hackam R, Akiyama H. Propagation velocity of pulsed streamer discharges in atmospheric air. IEEE Transactions on Plasma Science, 2003(31):1091–1094.

[57] Tsukamoto S, Namihira T, Hori H, Shinozaki K, Katsuki S, Hackam R, *et al*. An analysis of pulsed streamer discharge using a high-speed camera. Proceedings of Pulsed Power Plasma Science, Las Vegas, USA, 2001.

[58] Shimomura N, Wakimoto M, Togo H, Namihira T, Akiyama H. Production of ozone using nanosecond short pulsed power. Proceedings of the 14th IEEE International Pulsed Power Conference, Dallas, USA, 2003.

[59] Samaranayake WJM, Hackam R, Akiyama H. Ozone synthesis in oxygen using a pulsed discharge. Proceedings of Electrical Insulation Conference and Electrical Manufacturing & Coil Winding Conference, Cincinnati, USA, 2001.

[60] Samaranayake WJM, Miyahara Y, Namihira T, Katsuki S, Sakugawa T, Hackam R, *et al*. Pulsed streamer discharge characteristics of ozone production in dry air. IEEE Transactions on Dielectrics and Electrical Insulation, 2000(7):254–260.

[61] Ono R, Oda T. Formation and structure of primary and secondary streamers in positive pulsed corona discharge — Effect of oxygen concentration and applied voltage. Journal of Physics D-Applied Physics, 2003(36):1952–1958.

[62] Ono R, Oda T. Spatial distribution of ozone density in pulsed corona discharges observed by two-dimensional laser absorption method. Journal of Physics D-Applied Physics, 2004(37):730–735.

3

Chemical Kinetics and Oxidation Mechanisms Between O_3 and NO_x/SO_2/Hg

3.1 Introduction on Kinetics Modelling

Dynamics simulations and sensitivity analysis were performed by using the SENKIN module [1] in the CHEMKIN software package. The reaction rate of the branched-chain reaction varies under different conditions. Thus, to evaluate the chemical kinetics effect on reactions of ozone and NO_x/SO_2/Hg, varying various parameters to obtain a more correct choice of elementary reaction and kinetics parameters and a more precise modelling of reaction progress is defined and there related information is gathered during the modelling process. Meanwhile, the crucial factors, which comprise the reaction rate sensitivity, density sensitivity, and temperature sensitivity and have a significant effect on the reaction, are attached much more significance. Through sensitivity analysis, the limit rate reaction in the chemical reaction system can be obtained. Furthermore, relationships between various reactions and the importance of these interrelated reactions in the entire system can also be analyzed. The novel chemical kinetics mechanisms between ozone and flue gas components are to be uncovered finally.

So far, the research on chemical reaction mechanisms of O_3 and various pollutants in flue gas is still rarely reported. Based on our frontier research on this subject and the development in the crucial area of national interest, novel reaction mechanisms between ozone and typical flue gas are put forward firstly in the book. Here, the typical flue gas consists of NO_x, SO_2, Hg, HF, HCl, Cl_2, H_2S, HCl, CO, and so on (40 species in total). 40 species were attentively employed to study the chemical kinetics mechanisms between ozone and $NO_x/SO_2/Hg$. The 121 elementary reactions involved are first proposed here. The kinetic parameters of each elementary reaction are cited from the database of National Institute of Standards and Technology [2]. Table 3.1 shows a detailed schematic of the mechanisms and the related kinetic parameters.

Table 3.1   Detailed chemical reactions between O_3 and major pollutants of NO_x, SO_2, Hg, HF, HCl, H_2S, and CO in the typical flue gas

No.	Reactions	A	b	E (cal/mol)
1	$O_3+H=O_2+OH$	1.64E+13	0.8	750
2	$O_3+H=O+HO_2$	4.52E+11	0	0
3	$O_3+OH=O_2+HO_2$	1.15E+12	0	1990
4	$O_3+H_2O=O_2+H_2O_2$	6.62E+01	0	0
5	$O_3+HO_2=2O_2+OH$	1.19E+08	4.6	1380
6	$O_3+CO=O_2+CO_2$	6.02E+02	0	0
7	$O_3+N=O_2+NO$	6.00E+07	0	0
8	$O_3+NO=NO_2+O_2$	8.43E+11	0	2600
9	$O_3+NO_2=O_2+NO_3$	8.43E+10	0	4870
10	$O_2+O=O_3$	4.86E+13	−1.0	0
11	$O_3+O=2O_2$	4.82E+12	0	4090
12	$O_3+SO_2=O_2+SO_3$	1.81E+12	0	13910
13	$H+O_2+M=HO_2+M$	3.61E+17	−0.7	0
14	$H+H+M=H_2+M$	1.00E+18	−1.0	0
15	$H+H+H_2=H_2+H_2$	9.20E+16	−0.6	0
16	$H+H+H_2O=H_2+H_2O$	6.00E+19	−1.3	0
17	$H+OH+M=H_2O+M$	1.60E+22	−2.0	0
18	$H+O+M=OH+M$	6.20E+16	−0.6	0
19	$O+O+M=O_2+M$	1.89E+13	0	−1788
20	$H_2O_2+M=OH+OH+M$	1.30E+17	0	45500
21	$H_2+O_2=2OH$	1.70E+13	0	47780
22	$OH+H_2=H_2O+H$	1.17E+09	1.3	3626
23	$O+OH=O_2+H$	3.61E+14	−0.5	0
24	$O+H_2=OH+H$	5.06E+04	2.7	6290
25	$O+HO_2=O_2+OH$	1.40E+13	0	1073
26	$2OH=O+H_2O$	6.00E+08	1.3	0
27	$H+HO_2=H_2+O_2$	1.25E+13	0	0
28	$H_2O_2+H=HO_2+H_2$	1.60E+12	0	3800

29	$N+O_2=NO+O$	6.40E+09	1.0	6280
30	$N+OH=NO+H$	3.80E+13	0	0
31	$N+CO_2=NO+CO$	1.90E+11	0	3400
32	$NO+M=N+O+M$	9.64E+14	0	620910
33	$N+HO_2=NO+OH$	1.00E+13	0	8390
34	$NO+N=N_2+O$	3.27E+12	0.3	0
35	$NO+O(+M)=NO_2(+M)$	1.30E+15	-0.8	0
36	$NO+OH=HNO_2$	5.45E+17	0	0
37	$O+HNO_2=NO_2+OH$	1.21E+13	0	5938
38	$NO_2+NH_3=NH_2+HNO_2$	6.70E+08	3.4	29810
39	$H+HNO_2=HNO+OH$	7.57E+12	0.9	4914
40	$H+HNO_2=NO_2+H_2$	1.37E+12	1.6	6592
41	$H+HNO_2=NO+H_2O$	3.85E+11	1.9	3840
42	$O_3+HNO_2=2O_2+HNO$	3.01E+05	0	0
43	$HNO_3+O=NO_3+OH$	1.81E+07	0	0
44	$HNO_3+H=NO_3+H_2$	3.40E+12	1.5	16332
45	$HNO_3+H=NO_2+H_2O$	8.39E+09	3.3	6255
46	$HNO_3+NO=NO_2+HNO_2$	4.48E+03	0	0
47	$HNO_3+OH=NO_3+H_2O$	4.82E+08	0	0
48	$HNO_3+OH=NO_2+H_2O_2$	4.82E+08	0	0
49	$HNO_3=NO_2+OH$	6.90E+17	0	45730
50	$HNO+O=NO+OH$	2.29E+13	0	0
51	$HNO+HNO=N_2O+H_2O$	2.55E+07	4.0	1188
52	$HNO+H=NO+H_2$	2.70E+13	0.7	651
53	$HNO+NO_2=NO+HNO_2$	6.03E+11	0	1980
54	$HNO+OH=NO+H_2O$	4.82E+13	0	990
55	$NH_3+M=NH_2+H+M$	9.20E+15	0	84800
56	$NH_3+H=NH_2+H_2$	2.46E+13	0	17071
57	$NH_3+O=NH_2+OH$	1.50E+12	0	6040
58	$NH_2+OH=NH+H_2O$	1.25E+13	0	2200
59	$NH_3+OH=NH_2+H_2O$	3.25E+12	0	2120
60	$H+HNO=NH+OH$	2.00E+11	0.5	1300
61	$HNO+M=H+NO+M$	3.00E+16	0	48680
62	$NH_2+HNO=NH_3+NO$	5.00E+13	0	1000
63	$NH_2+NO=NNH+OH$	4.68E+19	-2.5	1876
64	$NH_2+NO=N_2+H_2O$	7.02E+19	-2.5	1876
65	$NH+O_2=HNO+O$	1.12E+12	0	3250

66	$NNH+M=N_2+H+M$	2.00E+14	0	20000
67	$NNH+NO=N_2+HNO$	5.00E+13	0	0
68	$NNH+OH=N_2+H_2O$	3.00E+13	0	0
69	$NH_2+NH_2=NH_3+NH$	6.30E+12	0	10000
70	$H+HO_2=OH+OH$	8.22E+12	0.8	0
71	$NO_2+HO_2=HNO_2+O_2$	2.20E-01	0	0
72	$NO+HO_2=HNO+O_2$	5.84E+05	0	5600
73	$NO+HO_2=NO_2+OH$	6.32E+11	0.6	1430
74	$NO+HO_2=HNO_3$	3.47E+12	0	−5720
75	$H_2O+2HO_2=2H_2O_2+O$	2.80E+13	0	32790
76	$H_2O_2+2HO_2=3O_2+2H_2$	6.03E+10	0	0
77	$SO_2+HO_2=SO_3+OH$	1.21E+07	0	0
78	$OH+HO_2=O_2+H_2O$	4.28E+13	−0.2	110
79	$HO_2+HO_2=H_2O_2+O_2$	1.87E+12	0	1540
80	$CO+HO_2=OH+CO_2$	1.50E+14	0	23650
81	$HO_2=H+O_2$	1.45E+16	−1.2	48490
82	$NO_3+HG=HGO+NO_2$	2.41E+09	0	0
83	$H_2O_2+2HG=2HGO+H_2$	5.12E+05	0	0
84	$O_3+HG=HGO+O_2$	1.80E+04	0	0
85	$HG+Cl+M=HGCl+M$	2.40E+08	1.4	−14400
86	$HG+Cl_2=HGCl+Cl$	1.39E+14	0	34000
87	$HGCl+Cl_2=HGCl_2+Cl$	1.39E+14	0	1000
88	$HGCl+Cl+M=HGCl_2+M$	2.19E+18	0	3100
89	$HG+HOCl=HGCl+OH$	4.27E+13	0	19000
90	$HG+HCl=HGCl+H$	4.94E+14	0	79300
91	$HGCl+HCl=HGCl_2+H$	4.94E+14	0	21500
92	$HGCl+HOCl=HGCl_2+OH$	4.27E+13	0	1000
93	$Cl+Cl=Cl_2$	2.00E+15	0	0
94	$Cl+HNO_3=NO_3+HCl$	1.21E+08	0	0
95	$Cl+H_2O_2=HCl+HO_2$	6.62E+12	0	1950
96	$Cl+H_2O=HCl+OH$	1.68E+13	0	17230
97	$Cl+NH_3=NH_2+HCl$	7.40E+10	0	0
98	$Cl+HCl=H+Cl_2$	1.00E+17	0	47490
99	$Cl+OH=O+HCl$	5.90E+12	0	5680
100	$Cl+HO_2=O_2+HCl$	1.08E+13	0	340
101	$Cl+H_2=H+HCl$	2.23E+13	0	4570
102	$HCl+F=Cl+HF$	4.21E+12	0	20

103	$HCl+NO_2=Cl+HNO_2$	3.98E+11	0	23450
104	$HCl+NO=Cl+HNO$	1.58E+13	0	50280
105	$HCl+O_3=HOCl+O_2$	2.83E+00	0	0
106	$F+F=F_2$	9.68E+10	1.0	−6340
107	$F+H_2O_2=HF+HO_2$	3.00E+13	0	0
108	$F+HNO_3=NO_3+HF$	3.61E+12	0	790
109	$F+NH_3=NH_2+HF$	1.63E+15	−1.6	240
110	$F+HO_2=O_2+HF$	5.00E+13	0	0
111	$F+H_2=H+HF$	6.62E+13	0	890
112	$O_3+H_2S=H_2O+SO_2$	1.58E+12	0	5210
113	$H_2S=S+H_2$	1.90E+14	0	65380
114	$CO+OH=CO_2+H$	1.51E+07	1.3	−758
115	$NO_2+NO_3=N_2O_5$	7.98E+17	−3.9	0
116	$N+NO_2=O+O+N_2$	1.30E-01	0	0
117	$NO_2+SO_2=NO+SO_3$	6.31E+12	0	27030
118	$NO_2+H=NO+OH$	2.41E+14	0	680
119	$NH+NO=N_2+OH$	3.53E+12	−0.5	120
120	$NO+NO=O_2+N_2$	3.10E+13	0	63190
121	$NO+N_2O=NO_2+N_2$	1.73E+11	2.2	46300

Note: The rate constant is obtained from the Arrhenius Equation $\{k=A\exp(-E/(RT))\}$, where A is called pre-exponential, E the activation energy, T denotes the system temperature, and R signifies the gas constant

As mentioned previously, definitely determining the most important branched-chain reaction among these interrelated reactions facilitates to better chose the elementary reaction and dynamics parameters, so as to ensure a more precise reaction process modelling. Meanwhile, the dominant parameters (including reaction rate sensitivity, density sensitivity, and temperature sensitivity), which play a critical role in reactions, are taken into account carefully.

The sensitivity analysis generally has two categories, i.e., PCAF (the principal component analysis of matrix F) and RIMP (the classic rate-of-production analysis), of which PCAF is usually adopted.

The reaction rate sensitivity (denoted by F_{ij} here) can be defined as

$$F_{ij} = \frac{\partial \ln f_i}{\partial \ln k_j},$$

where f_i is the production rate of the component I, and k_j is the reaction rate of the elementary reaction *j*.

The matrix F is denoted as the sensitivity matrix. The eigenvalues and eigenvectors of the matrix $F^T F$ are calculated. Each eigenvalue corresponds to an eigenvector, and each element of the eigenvector represents an elementary reaction. The absolute value of the eigenvector element represents the elementary reaction importance with respect to the species concentration.

3.2　Kinetic Modelling Results

3.2.1　Kinetic Modelling Between O₃ and NOₓ

NO_x-related chemical reactions are analyzed, and the key steps while O_3 oxidizes NO_x are determined necessarily. During the sensitivity analysis process, the gas components which are taken into consideration basically consist of 6.39% O_2, 204 ppm NO, and 5% H_2O. The balance gas is N_2 and the temperature is 150 °C. Results of the sensitivity analysis are shown in Figs. 3.1 – 3.4. The sensitivity analysis provides a variety of parameters for the quantitative analysis of modelling results. By analyzing the dimensionless sensitivity coefficient of different species, the importance of different elementary reactions in the production and consumption of various species can be essentially determined.

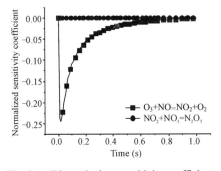

Fig. 3.1 Dimensionless sensitivity coefficients of O_3

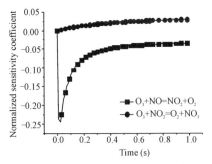

Fig. 3.2 Dimensionless sensitivity coefficients of NO

In Fig. 3.1, O_3 sensitivity coefficients change definitely over time. Within 0.2 s, the elementary reaction $O_3+NO=NO_2+O_2$ plays an important role on O_3 consumption. And in this time, the O_3 self-decomposition and reaction degree of

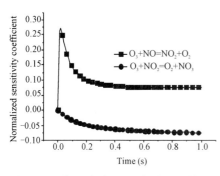

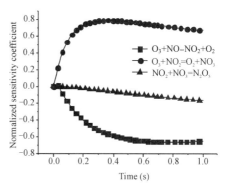

Fig. 3.3 Dimensionless sensitivity coefficients of NO_2

Fig. 3.4 Dimensionless sensitivity coefficients of NO_3

O_3 with other species are far lower than that of the mentioned elementary reaction. Figs. 3.2 and 3.3 show that the NO and NO_2 sensitivity coefficient curves are almost symmetrical; this observation indicates that O_3 directly oxidizing NO is a dominant pathway that producing NO_2. In Fig. 3.4, NO_3 is also the oxidation product of NO_2 and O_3. On the basis of the observations from Figs. 3.1 and 3.4, O_3 can be inferred to mainly react with NO but rarely with NO_2 when no excessive O_3 is provided. A high generation of NO_3 and N_2O_5 appears only under the conditions with excessive O_3. A comprehensive consideration of the foregoing analysis about Figs. 3.1 – 3.4 discloses the NO major oxidation pathway, as illustrated in Fig. 3.5. The arrow thickness in Fig. 3.5 describes the reaction intensity of the branch-chain reaction. Definitely, NO_3 and N_2O_5 are the senior states of NO oxidation reaction, which are generated via a step-by-sep oxidation of NO and only appear when O_3 is excessive. Additionally, the reaction of NO with HO_2 is able to generate HNO and then the HNO production is converted into N_2O.

The aforementioned sensitivity analysis determines several important elementary reactions, which are listed in a descending order of importance.

$$O_3+NO=NO_2+O_2 \tag{3.1}$$

$$O_3+NO_2=O_2+NO_3 \tag{3.2}$$

$$NO_2+NO_3=N_2O_5 \tag{3.3}$$

$$NO+HO_2=NO_2+OH \tag{3.4}$$

$$NO+HO_2=HNO_3 \tag{3.5}$$

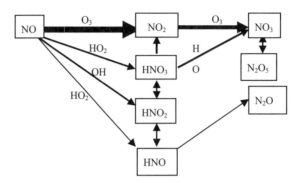

Fig. 3.5   Step-by-step path of NO_x oxidation with O_3

Compared with the above important reactions, other elementary reactions with less sensitivity are taken as unimportant chemical reactions and then omitted during the subsequent modelling process.

3.2.2   Kinetic Modelling Between O_3 and Hg

To evaluate the kinetic mechanism and determine the exact elementary reactions between ozone and mercury, the sensitivity analysis of mercury interrelated reactions is remarkably necessary. Accordingly, a typical gas compound with 0.01 μg/L of Hg vapor, 100 mg/(N·m³) of HCl, and 1 ppm of HF was considered. The dimensionless sensitivity coefficients of mercury are shown in Fig. 3.6. Definitely, mercury obtains the largest oxidation happened in the No. 82 reaction that given in Table 3.1 (i.e., the oxidation reaction between NO_3 and Hg). This means that the oxidation reaction is the strongest one among the mercury branch-chain reactions. As to the reaction between HCl and Hg, HCl is decomposed into Cl and Cl_2 firstly, which react with mercury to produce HgCl as a medium, then the medium is entirely converted into $HgCl_2$ as a final product. Based on the observations in Fig. 3.6, the oxidation paths of Hg with O_3 and HCl, respectively, are given in Fig. 3.7. Also, the arrow thickness represents the reaction intensity.

Resulted from the above sensitivity analysis determine the key elementary reactions of Hg oxidation as follows:

$$O_3 + NO = NO_2 + O_2 \tag{3.6}$$

$$O_3+NO_2=O_2+NO_3 \tag{3.7}$$

$$O_3+O=2O_2 \tag{3.8}$$

$$NO_3+Hg=HgO+NO_2 \tag{3.9}$$

$$Hg+Cl+M=HgCl+M \tag{3.10}$$

$$HgCl+Cl_2=HgCl_2+Cl \tag{3.11}$$

$$Cl+Cl=Cl_2 \tag{3.12}$$

$$Cl+OH=O+HCl \tag{3.13}$$

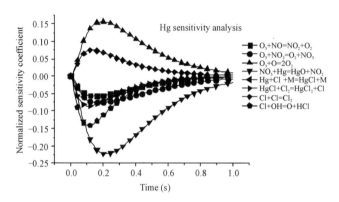

Fig. 3.6   Dimensionless sensitivity coefficient of Hg

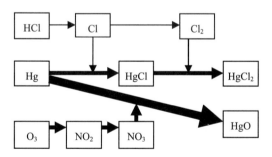

Fig. 3.7   Oxidation path of Hg

It should be noted that the above chemical reactions are reversible thoroughly. The foregoing analysis suggests that the Hg oxidation with HCl is mainly facilitated by Cl (this species generated by HCl and O free radicals) and the further conversion from HgCl to HgCl$_2$ essentially needs the Cl$_2$ assistance. This means that compared with HCl, the mercury oxidation is more sensitive to Cl$_2$ when adding Cl$_2$ into flue gas.   And the stronger mercury oxidation of Cl$_2$

(compared with HCl) has been experimentally confirmed by Gao *et al.* [3]. When O_3 exists, the reaction paths in Fig. 3.7 suggest that mercury oxidation dominantly depends on O_3, weakly dependent on Cl. Similarly, the reaction between O_3 and Hg is facilitated by the medium NO_3. And the NO_3 generation needs excessive O_3 from the previous analysis. Fortunately, the concentration of mercury is far lower than that of NO_x in the real-furnace flue gas. When injecting O_3 into flue gas for the NO_x oxidation, NO_3 can be spontaneously generated and only a little of the generated NO_3 can complete the mercury oxidation. Consequently, NO_x, SO_2, and mercury oxides are simultaneously removed through WFGD or alkaline scrubbers.

3.3   Oxidation Experimental Results

3.3.1   Experimental Setup

Although much crucial chemical kinetics information between O_3 and $NO_x/SO_2/Hg$ has been essentially elaborated above, further experimental investigations on oxidation reactions between them are still needed, so as to uncover the oxidation mechanisms more clearly. Accordingly, an ozone oxidation experimental system was established and shown in Fig. 3.8, which includes an ozone generator, mercury generator, quartz flow reactor, glass-made alkaline washing tower, and online gas analysis system. Ozone was generated by a DBD device with 3.7 – 4.0 kV AC voltage and 5 kHz frequency. The O_3 output concentration was continuously monitored by an ozone analyzer with a measuring range of 0 – 10000 ppm and precision of 1 ppm.

The simulated flue gas was prepared through N_2, along with a small amount of NO (0.6 vol.%) and SO_2 (1.5 vol.%). Oxygen was present in the main flow of the current test. Given that ozone was generated from an air source, oxygen was inevitably present in the reaction system. The gas flow rate was controlled by a mass flow controller (Qixing Huangchuang Co., China). The elemental mercury was generated from a mercury osmotic tube (VICI Metronics Co., USA), which was heated in a thermostatic water bath with 300 mL/min N_2 as the carrier gas.

The mixture of NO, SO_2, Hg, and N_2 reacted with O_3 in the quartz flow reactor, which was located in an electrically heated horizontal furnace with a heating length of approximately 600 mm. The quartz flow reactor, with its configuration

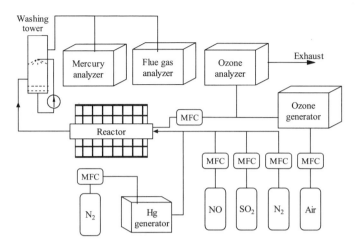

Fig. 3.8 Schematic of the experimental apparatus

presented in detail in Fig. 3.9, is a homocentric reaction tube with three channels and made with quartz glass to reduce the non-uniform temperature effect of the furnace. The reactor has a total length of 642 mm and an external diameter of 20 mm. Reactions proceed in the 100-mm-length and 5-mm-i.d. center tube (Item #5 in Fig. 3.9) which can be considered as an isothermal reactor. The $NO/SO_2/Hg$-enriched nitrogen gas flow entered into the reactor through Inlet 2 and then passed through a reciprocating preheating channel before entering the center tube. O_3 was introduced into the reactor through Inlet 1, which entered a separate preheating channel. The two well-preheated streams mixed with each other instantly at the nozzle of the center tube with high velocities because of the narrowing gas passage.

The washing tower is a 150-mm-length and 37-mm-i.d. glass-made cylinder, with a total volume of approximately 161 mL and running temperature of approximately 293 K. The alkaline absorber is filled with a 1 wt.% $Ca(OH)_2$ solution. A total of 1 L solution was used in one test. The alkaline solution were recycled by using a pressure pump and then sprayed into the tower through an atomizer nozzle at a flow rate of 0.5 L/min. The concentrations of NO, NO_2, O_2, N_2O, and SO_2 were analyzed by the continuous emissions monitors (CEMs) (Rosemount Analytical NGA2000, Emerson Process Management Co., Ltd.). The mercury content in the gas was monitored by mercury CEMs (Ms-1/dm-6a, Nippon Instrument Co.).

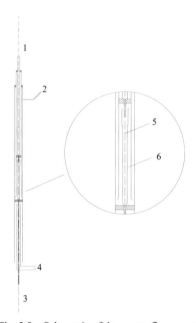

Fig. 3.9   Schematic of the quartz flow reactor
1) Inlet 1; 2) Inlet 2; 3) Outlet; 4) Air cooling; 5) Quartz flow reactor; 6) Preheat channels

The total flow rate of all reactants, including O_3 and the simulated flue gas, were fixed at 1000 mL/min. The residence time in the center tube ranged from 0.049 to 0.089 s and varied with the temperature calculated by $33.3K/T$ s, while that in the washing tower was approximately 9.7 s. The initial component concentrations used in the test were 215±10 ppm NO, 220±10 ppm SO_2, 4000±200 ppm O_3, and 50±0.5 µg/m^3 Hg, respectively.

3.3.2   *Oxidation Mechanism Between* O_3 *and NO*

In most practical flue gas, NO is the predominant nitrogen species of NO_x. Unlike NO, the other species such as NO_2, NO_3, and N_2O_5 are highly soluble in water, which can be captured in a SO_2 removal equipment, such as the WFGD system. Therefore, NO oxidation is the first step for the simultaneous removal of SO_2 and NO_x. When O_3 is injected into the center tube, NO in the flue gas can be oxidized into NO_2, NO_3, and N_2O_5, as shown in the following reactions:

$$NO+O_3=NO_2+O_2 \tag{3.14}$$
$$NO_2+O_3=NO_3+O_2 \tag{3.15}$$
$$NO_2+NO_3=N_2O_5 \tag{3.16}$$
$$NO+O+M=NO_2+M \tag{3.17}$$
$$NO_2+O=NO_3 \tag{3.18}$$

Among the five reactions, NO_2 is the main product when the O_3/NO stoichiometric ratio is smaller than 1.0 and this property has been confirmed by experimental results here. Results at temperatures ranging from 373 to 673 K are shown in Fig. 3.10. For the interference of NO_2, the ozone and NO_2 concentration detection module (UV) of CEMs is inaccurate and can only be considered as a nitrogen tracer. The oxidation products with respect to the O_3/NO stoichiometric ratio at 473 K are shown in Fig. 3.11. N_2O, NO_3, and N_2O_5 are minority products [4] to be measured difficultly. Therefore, only NO of NO_x is trusted in the present experiment. The NO in the original simulated flue gas was diluted with N_2. On the basis of observations in Fig. 3.10, NO can be effectively oxidized by ozone, but the result varies with temperature. The two lines of 373 and 473 K almost overlap, and nearly 85% of NO can be oxidized when 200 ppm ozone is added with a stoichiometric ratio of approximately 0.97. The oxidation rate increases almost linearly with the ozone level. Considering that ozone is a type of unstable gas that automatically decomposes into O_2 particularly at high temperature levels, Fig. 3.12 depicts the thermal decomposition property of the ozone-enriched gas. Experiments were conducted in a multi-sample glass tube with an oil bath for heat supplying. The initial ozone concentration was 4400±250 ppm. The temperature ranged from 298 to 523 K and residence time was 0.2 – 10 s. At room temperature (298 K), only 0.5% of ozone disappeared within 10 s. The decomposition rate dramatically increased with the temperature, particularly when the temperature reached 473 K. At 523 K, more than 80% of ozone decomposed within 1 s. At the same time, the residence time in the reactor decreased from 0.089 to 0.049 s when the temperature increased from 373 to 673 K. The two reasons thus decreased the NO conversion at 573 K.

Moreover, Fig. 3.10 shows that only 52.5% of NO can be oxidized at 573 K when 192 ppm ozone is in an atmosphere with the aforementioned stoichiometric ratio of approximately 0.89. At 673 K, almost no NO oxidation could achieve because of a strong ozone decomposition. Thus, in the future industrial application, the optimal temperature for the ozone injection technology, based on the present results, should be lower than 473 K. Meanwhile, only 0.09 s of residence time is needed. The temperature range that exists behind the air preheater is feasible and convenient for retrofitting boilers equipped with a WFGD system.

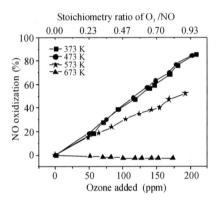

Fig. 3.10   NO oxidation property with ozone added at different temperatures

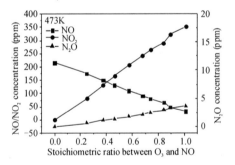

Fig. 3.11   By-products of NO oxidation by ozone at 473 K

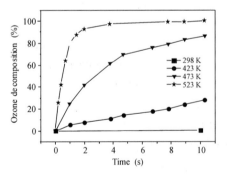

Fig. 3.12   Ozone decomposition rate at different temperatures

3.3.3 Oxidation Mechanism Between O_3 and SO_2

SO_2 is usually high in flue gas but dissolves more difficult than SO_3 does. When strengthening the reaction between O_3 and SO_2, the SO_2 absorption in a humid washer increases, but unfortunately, SO_2 participates in reactions among NO, Hg, and O_3, thereby increasing the O_3 consumption. In light of WFGD dealing with SO_2 efficiently, low energy consumption in a simultaneous multi-pollutants removal process necessitates the lowest reaction degree between SO_2 and O_3. Experiments here focus on the oxidation reaction between O_3 and SO_2 under conditions without catalysis, so as to understand the SO_2 oxidation mechanism related with O_3.

Experiments employed a tester similar to those in the previous oxidation experiments. Additionally, the SO_2 concentration was measured by a PG250 gas analyzer (Horiba) to avoid the interference of O_3 on the SO_2 absorption model. NO_x, SO_2, CO, and CO_2 were measured by using the infrared absorption method. The measuring range and precision of SO_2 were 500 and 1 ppm, respectively. The molar ratio of O_3 to SO_2 was 1.0 and temperature ranged from 27 to 400 °C. The original concentrations of SO_2 and O_3 were 34.8±5 and 1817±30 ppm, respectively.

Experimental results are shown in Fig. 3.13. It can be seen that the entire SO_2 oxidation efficiency is lower than 30% and effective oxidation temperatures are in 27 – 300 °C. The peak oxidation efficiency at 100 °C is 29.75%, whereas those at temperatures exceeding 300 °C are almost zero. This is because that O_3 decomposes into O_2 at relatively high temperatures and no longer participates in the reaction. Here the changing trend of the oxidation efficiency with temperature levels is similar to that in the NO oxidation experiments.

At 100 °C, comparisons of NO concentrations with and without SO_2 existence are shown in Fig. 3.14. At both two settings, the NO oxidation almost increases linearly with the ratio of O_3 to NO. No obvious change appears in the NO conversion rate when SO_2 is added, with the exception of slightly higher NO conversion rates (after the ratio above 0.3) appearing at the setting without SO_2. The slight difference is attributed to the SO_2 oxidation that consumes parts of O_3 while develops only a small effect on the final NO oxidation. In conclusion, the oxidation reaction rate between NO and O_3 is much higher than that of SO_2 and O_3. The presence of SO_2 has a small effect on the oxidation reaction between NO and O_3.

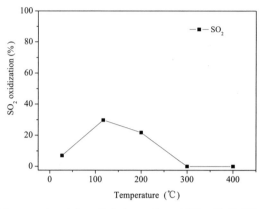

Fig. 3.13   Oxidize experimental results between O$_3$ and SO$_2$ with O$_3$/SO$_2$ = 1.0

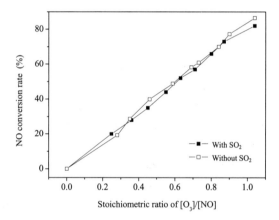

Fig. 3.14   Concentration variation in NO/O$_3$ reaction system after adding SO$_2$ (*T*=100 °C)

3.3.4   Oxidation Mechanism Between O$_3$ and Hg

Oxidized mercury (Hg^{2+}) can be easily trapped through WFGD, but removal of the elemental mercury (Hg^0) proves to be challenging. Although the proportion of each mercury species in gas phase varies with combustion conditions, coal types, and other factors, the absorption or oxidation of elemental mercury is still the key steps in improving the mercury removal efficiency in flue gas. Therefore, various types of reagents and methods have been developed to promote the elemental mercury oxidation. Apart from the oxidation of NO, O$_3$ and O can also efficiently convert Hg^0 into Hg^{2+}, as shown in the following reactions:

$$Hg^0+O_3=HgO+O_2 \qquad\qquad (3.19)$$

$$Hg^0+O=HgO \qquad\qquad (3.20)$$

Fig. 3.15 shows the experimental results of O_3 oxidizing Hg^0 at temperatures ranging from 423 to 573 K. Apparently, the elemental mercury can be efficiently converted into oxidized mercury by adding 50 – 100 ppm ozone (equaling to an O_3/Hg stoichiometric ratio of approximately 8900 – 17900). Thereafter, the oxidation rate increases slowly with the ozone concentration. From 423 K to 473 K, an approximately 25% increase can be observed in the mercury oxidation rate. The oxidation rate decreases a little as the temperature increases from 473 to 523 K. However, increasing further the temperature to 573 K decreases considerably the oxidation rate. Around 80% of Hg^0 can be oxidized with 80 ppm ozone (equaling to the stoichiometric ratio of approximately 14300) at 473 K. In contrast, relatively lower conversion rates nearby 55% appear at 423 and 573 K. Consequently, the optimal temperature range for Hg^0 oxidation should be 473 – 523 K, which is slightly different from that for NO oxidation. The above observations suggest that the Hg^0 oxidation rate initially increases but then decreases with the temperature. An explanation may rely on the decomposition of O_3 and HgO at higher temperatures, which counteracts the oxidation reaction.

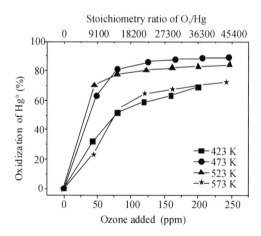

Fig. 3.15 Mercury oxidation properties by ozone at different temperatures

To uncover more clearly the causes of the changing trend of Hg^0 oxidation with respect to the temperature, Fig. 3.16 shows the equilibrium analysis of the HgO thermal decomposition property by FACTsage (a well-known software of chemical equilibrium analysis). The solid state of HgO begins to decompose at 700 K. This observation shows that the decreased mercury oxidation efficiency under 573 K is not caused by HgO decomposition and still rely on the decomposition of ozone itself.

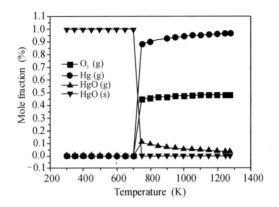

Fig. 3.16   Equilibrium analysis of the HgO decomposition

3.3.5   *Oxidation Mechanism Between O_3 and CO*

If O_3 effectively oxidizes CO in flue gas to raise the O_3 consumption, the oxidation of NO_x and Hg^0 is surely affected. Consequently, the CO concentration variation with the O_3 ejection has been studied so as to evaluate the CO oxidation properties. Within the experiment system graphed in Fig. 3.8, the original CO concentration, reaction temperatures, and total gas flux were 400 ppm, 100 – 300 °C, and 1 L/min, respectively. The residence time was $33.3K/T$ s (T denotes the unit of temperature, K). The flue gas composition was measured online by the Rosemont gas analyzer. The experimental data profile is presented in Fig. 3.17.

It can be seen that the CO concentration varies slightly when the ratio of O_3 to CO increases from 0.86 to 3.5 and temperature increases from 100 °C to 300 °C. This observation means that at temperature levels not exceeding 300 °C, no obvious CO oxidation reaction develops in the flue gas with O_3 ejection and thus its influence no the total O_3 consumption can be omitted.

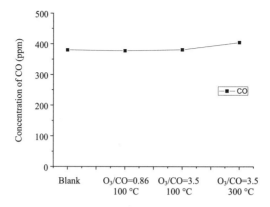

Fig. 3.17 CO concentration variations with the temperature and ratio of O_3 to CO

3.4 Competitive Reaction Mechanism Between Different Pollutants

3.4.1 Reaction Competition Between NO and SO_2 with Ozone

For the simultaneous removal of NO_x and SO_2, SO_2 inevitably exists during the NO oxidation process because of flue gas always containing high SO_2 content. The SO_2 influence on the NO oxidation should be investigated. As mentioned previously in the subsection 3.3.3, in the flue gas with ozone, SO_2 may also be oxidized into SO_3 by ozone or O radical. Reacting with the moisture in the flue gas, SO_3 then transforms into H_2SO_4, which increases the duct corrosion. Again, the SO_2 oxidation increases greatly the ozone consumption. The oxidation of SO_2 is essentially redundant because more than 95% of SO_2 in flue gas can be effectively removed by the WFGD system. Fortunately, the experimental results presented previously in the subsection 3.3.3 (see Fig. 3.14 and its discussion) have disclosed that the existence of SO_2 has little effect on the NO conversion. This observation implies weak reaction between O_3 and SO_2. Therefore, SO_2 in the flue gas affects slightly the total O_3 consumption in a simultaneous multi-pollutants removal system.

3.4.2   Reaction Competition Between NO and Hg^0 with Ozone

Both NO and Hg^0, existing in coal-fired flue gas, can be effectively oxidized by ozone or O radical. Therefore, the competition between NO and Hg^0 with ozone needs to be clarified. Hg^0 can also be oxidized by high-order nitrogen species, such as NO_2, and NO_3, as shown in the following reactions:

$$NO_2 + Hg = HgO + NO \tag{3.21}$$

$$NO_3 + Hg = HgO + NO_2 \tag{3.22}$$

Fig. 3.18 indicates the reactions between the ozone and a mixture of NO/Hg at 423 K. Apparently, the NO oxidation is easier than that of Hg^0. Almost all NO can be converted into higher order nitrogen species when the O_3/NO stoichiometric ratio is larger than 1.0. On the contrary, only a limited increase (from 12% to 39.7%) appears in the oxidation rate of Hg with increasing continuously the ozone concentration. These observations suggest that NO is prior to elemental mercury in the ozone oxidizing reaction competition. Apart from the direct oxidation of NO into NO_2, further NO oxidation reactions (such as the formation of NO_3 and N_2O_5) consume parts of the excessive ozone, which counteracts the Hg^0 oxidation to some extent.

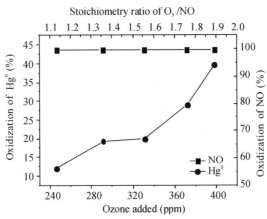

Fig. 3.18   Reaction competition between NO and Hg^0 with ozone, $T = 423$ K

3.5 Summary

This chapter focuses on the chemical kinetics and reaction mechanisms of ozone oxidizing the major flue gas components. In-depth investigations were performed through theoretic calculations and experiments. The acquired results are as follows:

(1) The specific chemical reaction mechanisms of ozone oxidizing the major flue gas components have been built. This relates to 40 flue gas species and 121 sub-reactions, including O_3, H_2O, O_2, NO_x, SO_2, Hg, HCl, Cl_2, HF, H_2S, CO, and so on. Sensitivity analysis reveals that the O_3-induced oxidation of NO_x is a stepwise process. At 150 °C, the Hg oxidizer depends mainly on NO_3, which is oxidized from NO_x. The Hg oxidation degree with O_3 is much higher than with Cl.

(2) The ozone decomposition starts at a much lower rate (i.e., the decomposition percentage of 0.5% per 10 s) at room temperature (298 K) and gradually increases with the temperature. At 523 K, the lifespan is only 2 s, whereas at 150 °C the decomposition percentage is 28% per 10 s and the half-life is 19.2 s. At 150 °C, the dynamics reaction time of ozone and NO_x is 0.6 s, which is shorter than the ozone decomposition time.

(3) The reaction mechanism of ozone and NO_x has been investigated. At temperatures below 200 °C, the ozone self-decomposition has no effect on the NO_x oxidation reaction. However, a relatively high temperature of 300 °C weakens the oxidation reaction because ozone has decomposed completely. In addition, no NO_x oxidation reaction occurs when the temperature reaches 400 °C. Based on the fact that the dynamics simulation results agree well with those acquired in experiments, here the established reaction mechanisms can be used in many other relative studies.

(4) The dynamics simulations of ozone oxidizing Hg^0 show that Hg^0 can be oxidized completely (i.e., HgO as the main bivalent format) under conditions with temperatures below 300 °C and the O_3/NO stoichiometric ratio of 1.5. A high mercury oxidation rate above 90% necessitates the O_3/NO stoichiometric ratio exceeding 1.2.

(5) The experimental results of O_3 oxidizing SO_2 show that the SO_2 oxidation efficiency is below 30% and the efficient temperature range is 27 – 300 °C. This means that SO_2 in flue gas is still absorbed mainly in the WFGD system if a simultaneous multi-pollutants removal system based on ozone is applied.

Meanwhile, it can be concluded that the SO$_2$ existence will affects slightly the total O$_3$ consumption.

(6) The experimental results of O$_3$ oxidizing CO uncover that almost no CO oxidation develops at temperatures below 300 °C and the CO existence also affects slightly the total O$_3$ consumption.

(7) NO is prior to elemental mercury in the ozone oxidizing reaction competition.

References

[1]   Kee RL, Rupley FM, Meeks E, Miller JA. CHEMKIN-III: A Fortran Chemical Kinetics Package for the Analysis of Gas-Phase Chemical and Plasma Kinetic. Sandia Report SAND96-8216, Sandia National Laboratories, New Mexico, 1996.

[2]   NIST. Chemical Kinetics Database on the Web: http://kinetics.nist.gov/index.php.

[3]   Gao HL, Luo ZY, Ni MJ, Cen KF. Experimental and mechanism study on mercury transformation and mercury removal in simulated combustion flue gases. Ph.D thesis of Zhejiang University, 2004.

[4]   Wang ZH, Zhou JH, Fan JR, Cen KF. Direct numerical simulation of ozone injection technology for NO$_x$ control in flue gas. Energy & Fuels, 2006(20):2432–2438.

4

Simultaneous Multi-Pollutants Removal with Ozone and Wet Scrubber

4.1 Introduction

The discussion above shows that the conversion of NO is a key process in any multi-pollutants control technique. The reaction kinetics of NO_x and O_3 has been mastered through our preliminary work. The main oxidation product of NO through O_3 is NO_2 and NO_3 or N_2O_5 can be generated only if excessive O_3 is injected. The NO_2 generation turns out to be the initial step of an ozone oxidation process integrated with WFGD system afterwards. It is no doubt that NO_x with a high valence, such as NO_2, have a strong water solvency. However, the solubility coefficient of NO_x is rather different from that of SO_2 because of the oxidation property of NO_x. NO_x vary the dissolution characteristic from SO_2 in several aspects. For example, the NO_2 solubility coefficient of 0.012 mol/(L·atm) (25 °C)[1] is lower than that of SO_2 (1.4 mol/(L·atm)) (25 °C) [2]. The existence of reductive substances (such as SO_3^{2-} and HSO_3) in a solution can increase a little the NO_2 absorption rate because of the oxidation property of NO_2 and redox reaction occurrence. Again, N_2O_5, which is the anhydride of nitric acid, can react quickly with water to form nitric acid as the product. Therefore, the removal of NO_x with a high valence (particularly NO_2) in a wet scrubber is investigated here, in addition to the interactions of NO_x with SO_2 and products generated. Given differences of the gas-liquid mass transfer characteristics between NO_x and SO_2, the attention necessitates to be focused on identifying whether a SO_2-favored alkali solution is appropriate to remove NO_x.

The removal of high-concentration NO$_x$ through solution absorption usually appears in the industrial generation of nitric acid [3–7], nitrate, or nitrite [8–11]. Under these circumstances, the high NO$_x$ concentration results in a high gas-liquid concentration gradient and the formation of some high-solubility diazo substances, such as N$_2$O$_4$ and N$_2$O$_3$ (with a high solubility coefficient of 1.6 and 26 mol/(L·atm) (25 °C) [12], respectively). Therefore, the mass transfer process keeps in good conditions and the absorption ratio is usually high. However, the removal of low-concentration NO$_x$ with such a solution absorption method is different. In this aspect, the published work [13–16] focused on using reductive substances (such as solutions with Na$_2$SO$_3$ or Na$_2$S) to enhance the mass transfer rate and little attention was paid on the pH-value effect, product analysis, and interactions of SO$_2$ and NO$_2$. A highlight of employing O$_3$ for the simultaneous removal of multi-pollutants in flue gas is that the existence of NO$_3$ or N$_2$O$_5$, generated at a case with excessive O$_3$, may greatly increase the mass transfer in te solution. However, no report on the liquid-phase absorption of these high-valence NO$_x$ substances is available because the multi-pollutants removal technology with O$_3$ has not yet been developed. Some related information in this aspect is discussed in this chapter.

In reactions between NO$_x$ and the absorption liquid, the mass transfer rate calculation follows the two-membrane theory for liquid phase chemical reactions and can be expressed as [17]

$$N_A = \beta \times k_L \times H \times P_i \qquad (4.1)$$

where β is the increasing factor of absorption reactions, k_L is the liquid-membrane mass transfer coefficient, H is the gas solubility coefficient, and P_i is the gas partial pressure at the gas-liquid interface. Eq. (4.1) suggests that besides the gas-liquid mixing conditions, two main factors from the properties of gas itself affects the adsorption rate, i.e., the gas solubility coefficient H and reaction rate between gas and the liquid phase. Essentially, a WFGD solution mainly contains H$^+$, Ca^{2+}, OH$^-$, SO$_2$·H$_2$O, SO$_3{}^{2-}$, HSO$_3{}^-$, CO$_3{}^{2-}$, and HCO$_3{}^-$, of which two factors may affect on the high-valence NO$_x$ absorption rate, i.e., the pH value (determined by concentrations of H$^+$ and OH$^-$) and the solubilized tetravalent S components in the solution (such as SO$_2$·H$_2$O, SO$_3{}^{2-}$, and HSO$_3{}^-$).

Generally, NO$_2$ is the dominant oxidation product of NO$_x$ when ejecting O$_3$

under stoichiometric conditions. Accordingly, the relatively low O_3 supply economizes the power consumption. Therefore, the attention in this chapter is initially focused on the sole NO_2 removal under traditional WFGD solution conditions. Effects of the pH value and reductive substances in the solution on the removal efficiency are studied, in addition to the determination of the optimal NO_2 removal conditions and a product analysis. Thereafter, the attention is focused on effects of the excessive O_3 conditions on the removal efficiency increase and the product species. Finally, a simultaneous NO_2 and SO_2 removal scheme combined O_3 oxidation with a two-tower scrubber is presented.

4.2 Experimental Section

Fig. 4.1 shows the experimental setup that combines O_3 oxidation with a wet scrubber. Oxygen flows into an ozone generator (CF-G-3-010g made by Guolin, Qingdao, China) to generate ozone. One part of the ozone flows into an ozone analyzer (IN2000, IN, USA) to show the ozone concentration. The other part enters into the simulated flue gas. NO, SO_2, and N_2 are supplied from each bottle, the properties of which are shown in Table 4.1. Each gas flow is separately controlled by a mass flow controller. The simulated flue gas, which is composed of NO, SO_2, and N_2, reacts with O_3 and then flows into the bottom of a 27-cm-height and 28-mm-i.d. scrubber tower. Placed within a flume, a specific solution (with the pH value and tetravalent-S concentration fixed) is pumped to the top nozzle (1/4-WXD-1.0-SS, made by Aogong, GuangZhou, China) of the scrubber tower by an acid/alkali-resistant pump (MG3004-W, made by Pasika, Nanjing, China). The flue gas flowing from bottom to top mixes with the solution before entering into a flue gas analyzer (Rosemount, NGA2000). The solution sample acquired in the tower bottom follows several steps before determining species concentrations: (i) adjusting the pH value into alkalescence; (ii) diluting the high ion concentrations if needed; (iii) anchored in a low temperature atmosphere; and (iv) analyzed by an ion chromatogram (792 Basic IC). Na_2SO_3, HCl, and $NaOH\backslash Ca(OH)_2\backslash CaCO_3$ were used to make absorption solutions with different compositions. NO_2 is produced when the molar ratio of O_3/NO is 1. Under these circumstances, NO_2 gas, used to replace ozone and NO, was thus employed directly to simplify the experimental setup. The total flow rate of the simulated flue gas was 1.5 L/min under the standard conditions, and that of the scrubber solution was fixed at 28 mL/min.

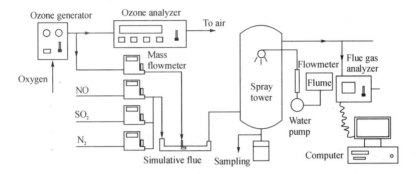

Fig. 4.1   Diagram of the experimental setup that combines O_3 oxidation with a wet scrubber

Table 4.1   Properties of the gases used in the experiments

Gas	Concentration	Volume/Pressure	Producer
N_2	High pure (99.999%)	40 L/15.0 MPa	Jingong Gas, Hangzhou
O_2	High pure (99.999%)	40 L/15.0 MPa	Jingong Gas, Hangzhou
NO/N_2	1.2%	8 L/9.5 MPa	Xinsiji Gas, Hangzhou
SO_2/N_2	1.2%	8 L/9.5 MPa	Xinsiji Gas, Hangzhou
NO_2/N_2	1.2%	8 L/9.5 MPa	Xinsiji Gas, Hangzhou
HCl/N_2	1.2%	8 L/9.5 MPa	Xinsiji Gas, Hangzhou

4.3   Effect of pH Value on NO_2 Removal

As mentioned above, NO_2 in the gas bottle was employed as an oxidation product when the molar ratio O_3/NO was 1 in the experiments. Given the inevitability of NO in the NO_2 gas from the bottle, the NO_2 gas employed actually comprised 300 ± 5 ppm NO_2 and around 10 ppm NO, with the gas phase balance controlled by Eqs. (4.2) and (4.3). This means that aside from NO_2 and NO, a little N_2O_3 and N_2O_4 exist in the gas phase. The EQUIL model of CHEMKIN 4.7 was employed before the experiments to calculate the balanced composition of the employed 300 ppm NO_x.

$$NO+NO_2 \xleftarrow{\quad K_1 \quad} N_2O_3 \tag{4.2}$$

$$NO_2+NO_2 \xleftarrow{\quad K_2 \quad} N_2O_4 \tag{4.3}$$

Fig. 4.2 shows the balanced compositions of NO_x at different ORs (i.e., the molar ratio of NO_2 to NO_x). The figure also shows that NO and NO_2 are the main components. When $OR = 1$, around 0.5 ppm N_2O_4 exists in the gas phase. The OR in the simulated flue gas is around 0.97, resulting in NO_2 accounting for 99.8% of the simulated NO_x. Therefore, this study mostly focuses on NO_2.

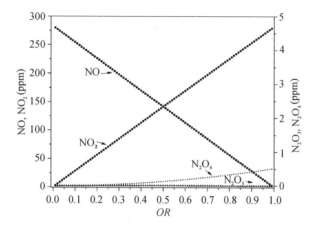

Fig. 4.2 Compositions of NO_x for different oxidation ratios

To evaluate the pH effect on the NO_2 removal, solutions with different concentrations of H ion were prepared, which include H^+, OH^-, and some inert hydroxyl ions. Under these circumstances, only pH can be taken as the potential factor that affecting the NO_2 removal. Accordingly, Fig. 4.3 illustrates the NO_2 removal performance with respect to pH.

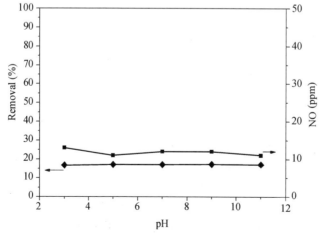

Fig. 4.3 Effects of the pH value on the removal of NO_2 and the concentration of NO at the exit (300 ppm NO_2 and 11 ppm NO)

Fig. 4.3 shows that a low NO_2 removal efficiency of around 17% appears at each pH setting. Similarly, Thomas and Vanderschuren [18] employed a padding tower with an alkali solution to absorb NO_x and also obtained a low removal efficiency of 12.9%. The low removal efficiency can be attributed to the low solubility coefficient of NO_2. According to the two-membrane mass transfer theory for gas and the liquid phases, the gas phase can reach a balance at the gas-liquid interface. A low NO_2 solubility coefficient develops a low NO_2 concentration at the liquid side of the interface, thereby declining the total mass transfer coefficient. Again, the reaction between NO_2 and water (shown in Eq. (4.4)) associated with the NO_2 concentration, is a two-step reaction with a relatively low reaction rate and limited increase in the NO_2 removal. Fig. 4.3 also uncovers that an increase in the pH value leads to a nearly constant NO_2 removal efficiency, which agrees well with the finding in the published work [19]. Patently, this result denotes that no connection exists between the pH value and the removal of NO_2 and N_2O_4. This observation can be mainly attributed to the fact that the hydrolysis reaction of NO_2 in the solution is hardly controlled by the pH value. The hydrolysis reaction mechanism of NO_2 can be definitely expressed as Eq. (4.5)[20]. Firstly, two NO_2 molecules produce $ON-O-NO_2$ through polymerization, isomerization, and reaction in Step a. Secondly, $ON-O-NO_2$ is combined with a H_2O molecule in Step b to form an intermediate. Thirdly, the intermediate is decomposed to HNO_2, H^+, and NO_3^- in Step c. Among the three reaction steps, Step a, which is not totally controlled by the pH value, is the main factor that decides the reaction rate.

$$2NO_2+H_2O=HNO_3+HNO_2 \tag{4.4}$$

$$2NO_2 \xrightarrow{a} \underset{O}{N}-O-\underset{O}{N} +H_2O \xrightarrow{b} \underset{\underset{H\ H}{O}}{\underset{|}{N-O-N}}\overset{O\ O}{\underset{O}{\diagup}} \xrightarrow{c} \underset{\underset{H}{O}}{\underset{|}{N}}\overset{O}{\diagup} +H^+ +NO_3^- \tag{4.5}$$

Fig. 4.4 shows the product concentration with respect to pH. It was found that the main N-components in the solution after adsorbing NO_2 were NO_2^- and NO_3^-. This observation fits well with the reaction in Eq. (4.4) and obviously, the molar ratio between the two N-contained products should be theoretically 1:1. Results in this figure also show that a slight molar concentration difference appears between the two N-contained ions and this difference decreases with pH. In comparison with NO_2^-, the slightly higher NO_3^- concentration at low pH levels is attributed to two reactions: (i) a part of the generated HNO_2 participates in its ionization reaction (as shown in Eq. (4.6)), where HNO_2 is a product of the NO_2 hydrolysate reaction presented in Eq. (4.4); (ii) the left unionized HNO_2 transforms into HNO_3, following the reaction shown in Eq. (4.7). A low pH facilitates the reaction balance in Eq. (4.6) to moves toward the left and thus increases the HNO_2 concentration. As a result, these circumstances accelerate the reaction in Eq. (4.7).

$$HNO_2=H^++NO_2^- \tag{4.6}$$

$$3HNO_2=HNO_3+2NO+H_2O \tag{4.7}$$

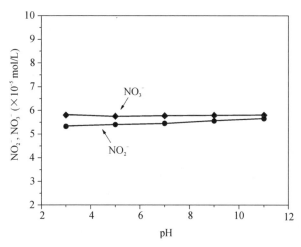

Fig. 4.4 Concentration of NO_2^- and NO_3^- in the solution at different pH values

Additional attention is needed to determine the effect of the reaction in Eq. (4.7) during the removal process. The aforementioned results have already uncovered that the NO concentration of remains around the initial value of 11 ppm at different pH values (Fig. 4.3); this indicates that the NO generated through the reaction in Eq. (4.7) is not considerable enough. The essentially low NO_x concentrations in the simulated flue gas actually develop a low HNO_2 concentration (usually around 10^{-5}) in the absorption solution, which can decreases further because of the occurrence the reaction in Eq. (4.6). Obviously, the resulted decomposition reaction in Eq. (4.7) is negligible [21], without affecting considerably the final removal efficiency. In consequence, a relatively strong HNO_2 decomposition process (finally resulting in a little higher NO_3^- concentration than that of NO_2^-) during a full experiment test should occur in the collection and storage stages of the absorption solution before ion chromatography measurements.

Fig. 4.5 shows the effects of the initial NO_2 concentrations on the removal efficiency by using water. The removal efficiency increases with the initial NO_2 concentration. This occurs because that with increasing the NO_2 concentration in the gas phase, the concentration gradient between gas and liquid increases and the partial pressure of NO_2 at the interface becomes larger. Consequently, the NO_2 solubility coefficient in liquid membrane increases, leading to an increased pattern appearing respectively in the reaction rate in Eq. (4.3) and in the NO_2 absorption rate. Finally, the NO_2 removal efficiency increases.

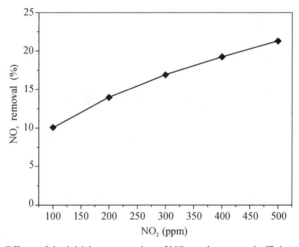

Fig. 4.5   Effects of the initial concentration of NO_x on the removal efficiency by water

4.4   Effect of Tetravalent-S Components on NO_2 Removal

It is thought that the existence of reductive substances in the WFGD solution, such as SO_3^{2-} and HSO_3^- of the solubilized SO_2 in the absorption liquid, can impel NO_2 to react with themselves, thereby increasing inevitably the removal efficiency by improving the enhancement factor in the chemical reaction absorption and advancing the mass transfer rate. In this subsection, the attention was initially focused on the Na_2SO_3 effect on the NO_2 removal in the solution, so as to validate the NO_2 removal improvement of reductive substances. Afterward, combined with the added Na_2SO_3, the pH effect was considered.

4.4.1 Effect of the Sole SO$_3{}^{2-}$

A series of Na$_2$SO$_3$ solutions with concentrations of 0 – 0.02 mol/L were used in the NO$_2$ removal experiments. Fig. 4.6 shows the acquired results. It can be seen that the NO$_2$ removal efficiency initially increases rapidly with the concentration within the concentration of 0 – 0.01 mol/L and then varies slightly. This result indicates that the redox reaction between SO$_3{}^{2-}$ and NO$_2$ plays a more important role in the increase of β (i.e., the increasing factor of absorption reactions, see Eq. (4.1)) than that of the NO$_2$ hydrolysis.

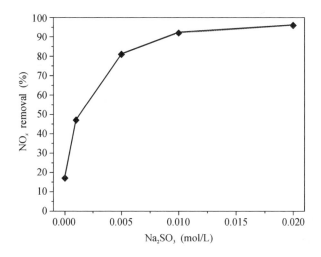

Fig. 4.6   NO$_2$ removal efficiency in different SO$_3{}^{2-}$ solution concentrations

Fig. 4.7 outlines the product analysis of the solution absorption with different SO$_3{}^{2-}$ concentrations. When the concentration is nil, the NO$_2$ hydrolysis (as shown in Eq. (4.4)) is the only reaction occurring in the system. The concentrations of NO$_2^-$ and NO$_3^-$ are matched (Fig. 4.4). After the appearance of SO$_3{}^{2-}$ in the liquid phase, the initial NO$_2^-$ concentration of 5.45×10^{-5} mol/L increases rapidly to 5.64×10^{-4} mol/L at the added SO$_3{}^{2-}$ concentration of 0.005 mol/L. Meanwhile, the NO$_3^-$ concentration decreases to an ultra-low level which is almost impossible to be detected. An explanation of these observations is provided. With the SO$_3{}^{2-}$ existence in the solution, the redox reaction between SO$_3{}^{2-}$ and NO$_2$ (generating a high NO$_2^-$ concentration) is much stronger that the NO$_2$ hydrolysis reaction (generating almost the same low concentration of NO_2^- and NO_3^-) in the liquid, resulting in a sharp increase in the NO_2^- concentration and a particularly low NO_3^- concentration.

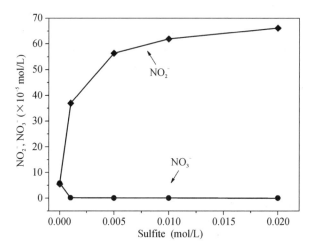

Fig. 4.7   Product of the absorption solution in different concentrations of SO_3^{2-}

4.4.2   Effect of pH with the Existence of Tetravalent-S Components

Definitely, the SO_2 removal performance will be better under an alkaline environment within a desulfurizer, but unfortunately, such a removal process is capable of blockage happening. Therefore, the solution pH value in a desulfurizer is often set at a weak acidity (e.g., pH 5 – 7) to ensure the dissolution rate of limestone particles [22,23]. Accordingly, evaluating the NO_2 removal performance under different pH values with the existence tetravalent-S components is necessary. The pH value was regulated but the total concentration of tetravalent-S components was kept at 0.01 mol/L to conduct the NO_2 removal experiments. The acquired results are shown in Fig. 4.8. The NO_2 removal efficiency significantly increases with the pH value. For example, the low removal efficiency of 52% at a pH value of 4 increases sharply to a high level of 83% at a pH value of 8. Evidently, here the pH-value effect on the NO_2 removal is different from that in subsection 4.3 (results in Fig. 4.3, without the existence of tetravalent-S components). A detailed explanation of these observations is as follows. Under the present solution conditions, two equilibrium reactions occur, as shown in Eqs. (4.8) and (4.9). An increase in the pH value means a decrease developing in the hydrogen ion concentration. Accordingly, the two equilibrium reactions move to a positive direction, which dissociate $SO_2 \cdot H_2O$ into HSO_3^-, and then HSO_3^- into SO_3^{2-}. Again, the reaction rate between NO_2 and SO_3^{2-} (Eq. (4.10)) is 40 times [24] of that between NO_2 and HSO_3^- (Eq. (4.11)). Consequently, the increasing factor of absorption reactions (i.e., β in Eq. (4.1)) increases, resulting a higher NO_2 removal efficiency. The pH influence on the NO_2 removal, in essence, is attributed to the concentration changes of the tetravalent-S components such as $SO_2 \cdot H_2O$, SO_3^{2-}, and HSO_3^- with respect to pH.

$$SO_2 \cdot H_2O = HSO_3^- + H^+ \tag{4.8}$$
$$HSO_3^- = SO_3^{2-} + H^+ \tag{4.9}$$
$$2NO_2 + H_2O + SO_3^{2-} = 2NO_2^- + 2H^+ + SO_4^{2-} \tag{4.10}$$
$$2NO_2 + H_2O + HSO_3^- = 2NO_2^- + 3H^+ + SO_4^{2-} \tag{4.11}$$

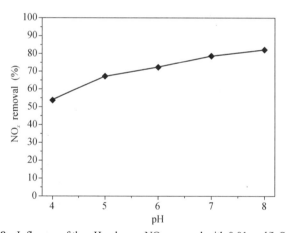

Fig. 4.8 Influence of the pH value on NO_2 removal with 0.01 mol/L S(IV) existence

Fig. 4.9 shows ion concentrations in the absorption solution. Concentrations of NO_2^- and NO_3^- gradually increases and decreases, respectively, as the pH value increases. This implies that SO_3^{2-}, which is prone to react with NO_2, develops an increase in its concentration, whereas the hydrolysis reaction (generating a low NO_3^- concentration) weakens to some extent. Consequently, reactions of NO_2 with the tetravalent-S components strengthen, leading to an increasing contribution of the redox reactions in the total NO_2 removal.

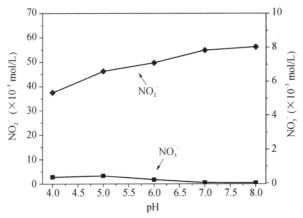

Fig. 4.9   Concentration of ions at different pH values with the existence of S(IV)

4.4.3 *Effect of the Initial NO$_2$ Concentration*

Experiments were carried out with typical solution parameters (i.e., a pH value of 5.5 with 0.01 mol/L tetravalent-S existence) that are usually used in desulfurizers. Fig. 4.10 shows the removal efficiency variation with the initial concentration of NO$_2$. The removal efficiency decreases a little from 74 to 68% as the initial NO$_2$ concentration increases from 100 to 400 ppm. The variation behavior of the concentration ratio of NO$_2^-$/NO$_3^-$ can also be analyzed from this figure. The NO$_2^-$/NO$_3^-$ concentration ratio actually represents the comparison between the redox reactions and NO$_2$ hydrolysis. It is concluded that advancing the two reactions in Eqs. (4.10) and (4.11) can increase the ratio, while strengthening the NO$_2$ hydrolysis, on the contrary, decreases the ratio value. The figure shows that the NO$_2^-$/NO$_3^-$ ratio decreases from 220 to 78 as the initial NO$_2$ concentration increases from 100 to 400 ppm; this means that the proportion of the redox reactions decreases. The reaction rates in Eqs. (4.10) and (4.11) can be expressed as $k=k_o\times[S(IV)]\times[NO_2]$. With increasing the NO$_2$ concentration and maintaining the total tetravalent-S (denoted by S(IV) here) concentration, both the first order reaction rate constant $k_o\times[S(IV)]$ of NO$_2$ and β remain constant, while the absorbed NO$_2$ increases, thus increasing the S(IV) depletion in the solution. Accordingly, the concentration of H$^+$ generated from reactions in Eqs. (4.10) and (4.11) increases. These circumstances favor the occurrence of the reverse reactions listed in Eqs. (4.8) and (4.9), thereby decreasing the NO$_2$ consumption in the redox reactions. Consequently, the ratio of NO$_2^-$/NO$_3^-$ decreases clearly with the initial NO_2 concentration, accompanied by a small drop in the NO_2 removal efficiency.

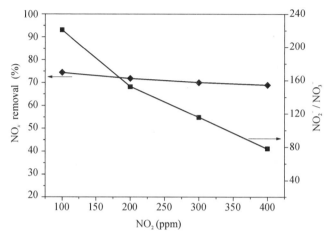

Fig. 4.10 NO_2 removal efficiency at different initial concentrations with the existence of S(IV)

4.5   Simultaneous Removal of SO₂ and NO₂

Obviously, the SO_2 absorption in the liquid phase mostly leads to an increase in the tetravalent-S concentration and a decrease in the pH value. Meanwhile, the NO_2 absorption behavior lowers both the pH value and tetravalent-S concentration. The interactions between SO_2 and NO_2 must be clearly understood so as to increase the simultaneous removal efficiencies of multi-pollutants.

4.5.1   Effect of SO₂ on NO₂ Removal

In the related experiments, the pH value and tetravalent-S concentration was kept at 5.5 and 0.01 mol/L, respectively, while the SO_2 concentration was adjusted within 0 – 500 ppm to form a series of test settings. As shown in Fig. 4.11, results suggest that the SO_2 effect on the NO_2 removal efficiency is negligible. That is, the removal efficiency slightly decreases from 70% to 67% as the SO_2 concentration increases in 0 – 500 ppm. This observation occurs because of the dual roles of the SO_2 absorption: (i) promoting the reactions listed in Eqs. (4.10) and (4.11) by increasing the tetravalent-S concentration; (ii) decreasing the pH value and thus reversing the reactions listed in Eqs. (4.8) and (4.9). The competition of the dual-roles finally results in the slightly negative effect of SO_2 on the NO_2 removal efficiency.

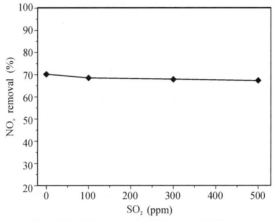

Fig. 4.11 NO_x removal efficiency with SO_2 coexistence

Fig. 4.12 uncovers the SO_2 effect on the NO_2 absorption products. It can be seen that with increasing SO_2 from 0 to 500 ppm, both the NO_2^- and NO_3^- concentrations vary slightly all the while (i.e., a slight decrease from 4.9×10^{-4} to 4.5×10^{-4} mol/L and the corresponding increase from 5×10^{-6} to 1.1×10^{-5} mol/L for the former and latter, respectively). These changes indicate that the proportion of the NO_2 redox reactions becomes smaller and that of the NO_2 hydrolysis is enhanced.

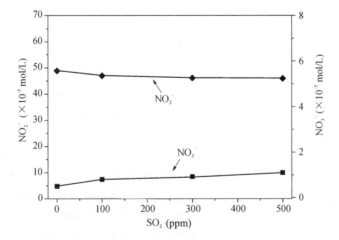

Fig. 4.12   Influence of SO_2 on the absorption product of NO_2

4.5.2 Effect of NO_2 on SO_2 Removal

Under the same liquid conditions as those in Fig. 4.11, the experimentally-determined NO_2 influence on the SO_2 removal and product concentration is presented in Fig. 4.13. The SO_2 removal efficiency slightly decreases from 96.5% to 92.6% as the NO_2 concentration increases from 0 to 300 ppm. The nitrous and nitric acid generation, produced through the reactions in Eqs. (4.4), (4.10), and (4.11) when NO_2 enters the liquid phase, increases the H^+ concentration and decreases the pH value. Under flue gas conditions where the NO_x concentration is clearly smaller than that of SO_2, the influence of the NO_2 adsorption on the H^+ concentration and pH value is weak, finally resulting in a slight decrease in the SO_2 removal with the NO_2 concentration. However, the change of SO_4^{2-} concentration is noticeable in Fig. 4.13. It should be noted that a 1.2×10^{-5} mol/L SO_4^{2-} concentration appears under the circumstances without NO_2. An explanation may lies in the potential oxidation of tetravalent-S components through the oxygen dissolved in the solution. With increasing NO_2, reactions between NO_2 and tetravalent-S components occur, resulting in an apparent increase in the SO_4^{2-} concentration (reaching 1.42×10^{-4} mol/L at 300 ppm NO_2). In practical desulfurizer's operations, it is accepted that the NO_2 existence is beneficial to the change in SO_2 and can increase the plaster output.

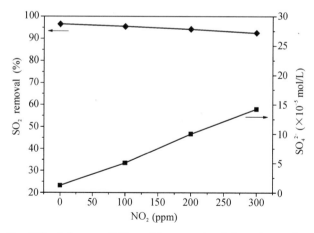

Fig. 4.13 Influence of NO_2 on SO_2 removal and absorption product

4.6   NO$_x$ Wet Removal with Excess Ozone Oxidization

The above investigations into the NO$_2$ removal were conducted for the circumstances where the molar ratio of O$_3$ to NO is equal to 1 and NO$_2$ is the main component of NO$_x$. The removal efficiency under the circumstances is usually below 70%. In light of the increasingly stricter discharge standards, there essentially exists space for a further NO$_x$ removal by increasing the ozone supply. Accordingly, here the experiments were conducted with high-valence NO$_x$ (generated with $x>2$) to evaluate the removal efficiency; that is, the molar ratio of O$_3$ to NO exceeds 1. The pH value of 5 and tetravalent-S concentration of 0.01 mol/L were kept in the liquid phase. The fed SO$_2$ and NO concentrations were 500 and 300 ppm, respectively. The high-valence NO$_x$ were generated through ozone injection.

Fig. 4.14 shows the NO$_x$ and SO$_2$ removal efficiencies as the function of the molar ratio of O$_3$/NO. The effect of the molar ratio of O$_3$/NO on various ion concentrations is depicted in Fig. 4.15. In Fig. 4.14, it can be seen that the NO$_x$ removal efficiency increases from 49.5 to 63% when the molar ratio increases from 0.7 to 1.0 because of a NO$_2$ increase in NO$_x$. After the molar ratio exceeds 1, increasing the molar ratio still enhances the NO$_x$ removal, but with a greater increase rate compared with that under the previous circumstances; this observation indicates that under excess ozone conditions, the generated NO$_x$ have some components with greater solubilities than that of NO$_2$. An explanation is provided in detail. With a molar ratio exceeding 1, the main reactions affecting the NO$_x$ removal consist of Eqs. (4.12) – (4.14) listed below. First, NO$_2$ is oxidized by O$_3$ to NO$_3$. Then the generated NO$_3$ combines with NO$_2$ to forms N$_2$O$_5$. Finally, N$_2$O$_5$ reacts with H$_2$O to produce nitric acid with an infinite solubility coefficient. The occurrence of these three reactions improves the removal efficiency by speeding up the NO$_x$ absorption rate.

$$NO_2 + O_3 = NO_3 + O_2 \qquad (4.12)$$

$$NO_3 + NO_2 = N_2O_5 \qquad (4.13)$$

$$N_2O_5 + H_2O = 2HNO_3 \qquad (4.14)$$

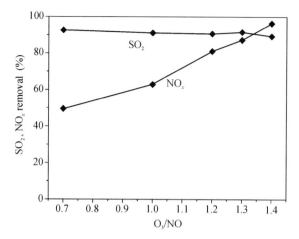

Fig. 4.14 NO$_x$ and SO$_2$ removal efficiency at different molar ratios of O$_3$/NO

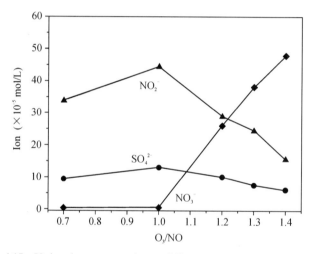

Fig. 4.15 Various ion concentrations at different molar ratios of O$_3$/NO

Meanwhile, the ion concentrations depicted in Fig. 4.15 show that with increasing the molar ratio within 0.7 – 1.0, a particularly low the NO$_3^-$ concentration appears and varies slightly, while the NO$_2^-$ concentration increases. These observations occur because the increasing NO$_2$ content takes part in the redox reactions with tetravalent-S components. After the molar ratio exceeds 1.0, the NO$_3^-$ and NO$_2^-$ concentrations rapidly increase and decrease with the molar ratio, respectively. These findings are attributed to the fact that with the excessive O$_3$ existence, the generated N$_2$O$_5$ reacts with H$_2$O to produce a considerable dosage of nitric acid through the aforementioned reactions in Eqs. (4.12) – (4.14), thereby reducing the NO_2 content that participates in the redox reactions. As a result, the NO_3^- concentration greatly increases, whereas that of NO_2^- decreases rapidly. Fig. 4.14 also shows that the SO_2 removal efficiency generally decreases slightly with the molar ratio of O_3/NO all the while. The explanation of the mild SO_2 removal change within the molar ratio 0.7 – 1.0 is the same as that in the corresponding discussion about Fig. 4.13 and is not repeated here. While for the circumstances with the molar ratio above 1.0, on one side, the nitric acid generated in the liquid phase blocks the SO_2 absorption because of an increase in the hydrogen ion concentration, on the other hand, a mild reaction between ozone and SO_2 in water [25,26] can increase a little the SO_2 removal. The combined result is that the SO_2 removal efficiency still varies slightly. Fig. 4.15 also shows that the SO_4^{2-} concentration increases through the NO_2 oxidization behavior as the molar ratio increases within 0.7 – 1.0. Increasing further the molar ratio, on the contrary, decrease the SO_4^{2-} concentration because of the lessened NO_2 oxidization with tetravalent-S components (see the rapidly-decreasing NO_2^- concentration pattern). However, the SO_4^{2-} concentration reduces less obviously compared with the NO_2^- concentration because of the partial tetravalent-S components oxidized by ozone and the NO_3 dissolved in water.

4.7   Simultaneous Desulfurization and Denitrification Scheme Incorporated with Ozone Oxidization and Dual-Tower Scrubbing

As discussed previously, the typical flue gas components of SO_2 and NO_x change to solubilized salt ions of NO_3^-, NO_2^-, and SO_4^{2-} after a combined process of ozone oxidization and liquid phase absorption in a scrubbing tower. It was found that the NO_3^- concentration greatly increased owing to the N_2O_5 absorption in the solution when the molar ratio of O_3/NO exceeds 1.0. With the NO_x ($x>2$) absorption solely appearing in the solution, nitric acid, nitrate, and nitrite are consequently generated. To achieve simultaneously desulfurization and denitrification in flue gas and recycle the absorption products in scrubbing towers, a flue gas treatment method combined ozone oxidization and two-tower scrubbing and its setup thereof were put forward [27]. The key operational principle of the proposed setup is that the separation of sulfur and nitrogen is accomplished based on the different solubility levels between NO and SO_2. Accordingly, the respective absorption, oxidization, and byproduct recycle are then conducted in the two scrubbing towers.

Fig. 4.16 shows the schematic of the setup used for a real flue gas treatment based on the method in [27]. Flue gas emitted from a furnace is cooled in a heat exchanger 2 and then passes through scrubbing towers 3 and 11, respectively, where SO_2 and NO_x are respectively absorbed and recycled by alkali liquids. The remaining flue gas is sent back to the heat exchanger 2 for heating before being discharged into the chimney. High-concentration ozone is generated in an ozone generator 4 by blowing in air or oxygen. The partial ozone entering the liquid phase in a scrubbing tower 3 oxidizes tetravalent-S components. Sulfur is recycled as sulfate with high valences. To save the ozone consumption, a replaceable way for oxidizing tetravalent-S components is to fan air into the scrubbing tower 3. The left ozone is sent into the flue gas flow before entering a scrubbing tower 11. The molar ratio of this ozone input to NO_x in the flue gas flow is set at $0.5 - 1.5$, depending on the denitrification products and absorbent liquid in the scrubbing tower 11. Byproducts (i.e., nitric acid through water recycling absorption and nitrate/nitrite through alkali liquor absorption, respectively) can be obtained by transforming the low-valence and weak-water-solubility NO_x (with NO accounting for the major share and a little NO_2) into the high-valence and high-water-solubility oxidized forms (such as NO_2 and N_2O_5).

The byproduct of nitric acid can be obtained through water absorption in the scrubbing tower 11 with the O_3/NO molar ratio of around 1.5. The experimental investigation [28] into producing nitric acid through ozone solely oxidizing NO in flue gas has indicated that increasing the molar ratio of O_3/NO produces more nitric acid and simultaneously restrains the nitrous acid generation. Within the common exhaust gas temperature range, O_3 and NO_3 concentrations decrease as the reactive time in the gas phase prolonged because of two negative reactions (i.e., O_3 reacting with NO_3 and the NO_3 molecule reacting with itself). As a result, the nitric acid production decreases. In the practical application, O_3 and NO_3 should enter the wet removal device as soon as they thoroughly mix, thereby shortening greatly their residence times before entering the scrubbing tower 11. Similarly, the injecting temperature should be as low as possible to enhance the nitric acid yield because a low flue gas temperature facilitates to reduce the consumption of O_3 and NO_3 in gas phase reactions. Because the N_2O_5 absorption is independent of the pH value, the nitric acid yield is affected slightly by the pH value of the solution, favoring an acid solution recycling scrubbing process.

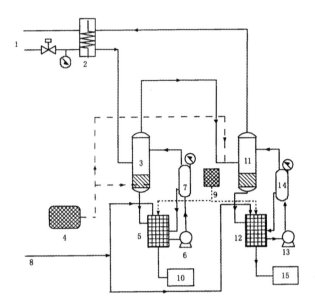

1. Boiler flue; 2. Heat exchanger; 3. SO_2 scrubber; 4. Ozone generator; 5. Liquid buffer tank; 6. Caustic circulation pump; 7. Lye spray stable volt; 8. Process water; 9. Liquid tank; 10. Crystallizing system; 11. NO_x scrubber; 12. Liquid buffer tank; 13. Caustic circulation pump; 14. Lye spray stable volt; 15. Crystallizing (collect) system

Fig. 4.16   Schematic process of desulfurization and denitrification through ozone oxidization combined with two-tower scrubbing[27]

4.8   Summary

In this chapter, the removal performance of dissoluble high-valence NO_x (specifically NO_2) via an alkali liquid scrubbing method was investigated, in addition to (i) interactions between NO_x and SO_2 in adsorption reactions and (ii) the changing trends of the adsorption product species and concentration. Accordingly, effects of various factors such as the pH value, reductive tetravalent-S existence and its concentration, NO_2 initial concentration, ozone injection dosage, and interactions of NO_2 and SO_2 were experimentally evaluated so as to determine favorable NO_x and SO_2 removal conditions. Important results are summarized as below.

(1) The NO_2 absorption is not obviously affected by the pH value. The NO_2 removal efficiency is strongly dependent on the NO_2 hydrolysis reaction and solubility coefficient. Accordingly, nitric acid and nitrous acid are the main absorption products. Exceptionally, the NO_2 removal efficiency decreases a little

with increasing the NO_2 initial concentration. Increasing the molar ratio of O_3/NO enhances the NO_x absorption removal. Especially, as the mole ratio reaches to 1.4, the NO_2 removal efficiency jumps to 96%. Ozone oxidization effectively helps to convert NO_2 into N_2O_5 but is insensitive to SO_2. Consequently, increasing the ozone dosage advances greatly the NO_x lye-absorption removal and barely impact on the SO_2 removal efficiency.

(2) Adding reductive tetravalent-S components with a concentration below 0.01 mol/L greatly increases the NO_2 removal efficiency. The redox reactions of NO_2 and tetravalent-S components are the dominant reactions related with NO_2 in the liquid phase and generate a high NO_2^- concentration. A high pH value increases the SO_3^{2-} concentration and improves the NO_2 absorption rate. However, the NO_2 removal efficiency is found to be around 70% under the typical liquid phase conditions appearing in desulfurization towers.

(3) The existence of SO_2 weakens slightly the NO_2 removal. In comparison with an atmosphere without SO_2, the denitrification efficiency in the simulated flue gas is reduced by only 3% when 500 ppm SO_2 is added. Accordingly, SO_2 also results in negligible effects on absorption products of NO_2. The existence of NO_2 also weakens a little the SO_2 removal. However, the NO_2 negative effect on the SO_2 removal seems to be a little stronger. That is, the desulfurization efficiency can be reduced by 4% when 300 ppm NO_2 is co-absorbed. The sulfate produced in the solution uplifts owing to the oxidation of NO_2.

(4) A simultaneous desulfurization and denitrification method incorporated with ozone oxidization and dual-tower scrubbing and its setup thereof were put forward previously. Here the schematic of the setup for a real-furnace flue gas treatment and the introductory material about the technological process is repeated in detail. Again, some important results in the published work is presented to disclose (i) the factors that affecting that removal efficiencies, (ii) favorable scrubbing solution conditions for recycling the byproducts, and (iii) measures to improve the O_3 oxidization performance for a less O_3 dosage consumed.

References

[1] Chameides WL. The photochemistry of a remote marine stratiform cloud. Journal of Geophysical Research: Atmospheres, 1984(89):4739–4755.
[2] Weast RC, Astle MJ, Beyer WH. CRC Handbook of Chemistry and Physics. Cleveland: CRC Press, 1988.

[3] Hüpen B, Kenig EY. Rigorous modelling of NO_x absorption in tray and packed columns. Chemical Engineering Science, 2005(60):6462–6471.

[4] Jethani KR, Suchak NJ, Joshi JB. Modeling and simulation of a spray column for NO_x absorption. Computers & Chemical Engineering, 1992(16):11–25.

[5] Pradhan MP, Suchak NJ, Walse PR, Joshi JB. Multicomponent gas absorption with multiple reactions: modelling and simulation of NO_x absorption in nitric acid manufacture. Chemical Engineering Science, 1997(52):4569–4591.

[6] Ramanand SB, Rao DP. Modelling and simulation of NO_x absorption into water in a countercurrent flow packed column. Computers & Chemical Engineering, 1996(20):1059–1063.

[7] Counce RM, Perona JJ. Scrubbing of gaseous nitrogen oxides in packed towers. AIChE Journal, 1983(29):26–32.

[8] Suchak NJ, Jethani KR, Joshi JB. Absorption of nitrogen oxides in alkaline solutions: Selective manufacture of sodium nitrite. Industrial & Engineering Chemistry Research, 1990(29):1492–1502.

[9] Pradhan MP, Joshi JB. Absorption of NO_x gases in aqueous NaOH solutions: Selectivity and optimization. AIChE Journal, 1999(45):38–50.

[10] Pradhan MP, Joshi JB. Absorption of NO_x gases in plate column: Selective manufacture of sodium nitrite. Chemical Engineering Science, 2000(55):1269–1282.

[11] Paiva JLD, Kachan GC. Absorption of nitrogen oxides in aqueous solutions in a structured packing pilot column. Chemical Engineering and Processing, 2004(43):941–948.

[12] Durham JL. Influence of gaseous nitric acid on sulfate production and acidity in rain. Atmospheric Environment, 1981(15):1059–1068.

[13] Yamamoto T, Okubo M, Nagaoka T, Hayakawa K. Simultaneous removal of NO_x, SO_x, and CO_2 at elevated temperature using a plasma-chemical hybrid process. IEEE Transactions on Industry Applications, 2002(38):1168–1173.

[14] Nash T. The effect of nitrogen dioxide and of some transition metals on the oxidation of dilute bisulfite solutions. Atmospheric Environment, 1979(13):1149–1154.

[15] Wu ZB, Wang HQ, Liu Y, Jiang BQ, Sheng ZY. Study of a photocatalytic oxidation and wet absorption combined process for removal of nitrogen oxides. Chemical Engineering Journal, 2008(144):221–226.

[16] Shen CH, Rochelle GT. Nitrogen dioxide absorption and sulfite oxidation in aqueous sulfite. Environmental Science & Technology, 1998(32):1994–2003.

[17] Zhang CF. Gas-Liquid Reaction and Reactor. Beijing: Chemical Industry Press, 1985.

[18] Thomas D, Vanderschuren J. Nitrogen oxides scrubbing with alkaline solutions. Chemical Engineering & Technology, 2000(23):449–455.

[19] Patwardhan JA, Joshi JB. Unified model for NO_x absorption in aqueous alkaline

and dilute acidic solutions. AIChE Journal, 2003(49):2728–2748.

[20] Kameoka Y, Pigford RL. Absorption of nitrogen dioxide into water, sulfuric acid, sodium hydroxide, and alkaline sodium sulfite aqueous solutions. Industrial & Engineering Chemistry Fundamentals, 1977(16):163–169.

[21] Park JY, Lee YN. Solubility and decomposition kinetics of nitrous acid in aqueous solution. Journal of Physical Chemistry, 1988(92):6294–6302.

[22] Zhu SY. Environmental and Industrial Gas Purification. Beijing: Chemical Industry Press, 2001.

[23] Li GC. Air Pollution Control Technology. Beijing: Chemical Industry Press, 2001.

[24] Takeuchi H, Ando M, Kizawa N. Absorption of nitrogen oxides in aqueous sodium sulfite and bisulfite solutions. Industrial & Engineering Chemistry Process Design and Development, 1977(16):303–308.

[25] Hoffmann MR. On the kinetics and mechanism of oxidation of aquated sulfur dioxide by ozone. Atmospheric Environment, 1986(20):1145–1154.

[26] Botha CF, Hahn J, Pienaar JJ, Vaneldik R. Kinetics and mechanism of the oxidation of sulfur(IV) by ozone in aqueous solutions. Atmospheric Environment, 1994(28):3207–3212.

[27] Wang ZH, Bai YF, Cen KF, Zhou JH, Wu SZ, Zhou ZJ, *et al.* Simultaneous desulfurization and denitrification method incorporated with ozone oxidization and two-tower scrubbing and its setup thereof. China Patent, No.: 200910095344.4, 2009.

[28] Jiang SD, Wang ZH, Zhou JH, Yang WJ, Cen KF. Experimental research on production of nitric acid using ozone denitration flue gas. Journal of Combustion Science and Technology, 2010(16):57–61.

5

Application and Economic Analysis of the Multi-Pollutants Removal Technology Incorporated with Ozone Oxidization and Alkali Solution Adsorption

5.1   Application Scheme of O_3 and FGD

The up-to-date and advanced method, removal of multi-pollutants in flue gas by ozone oxidation, coupled with the existing FGD system, has hardly possible destroy the boiler's daily operations, let alone interfere the combustion efficiency. Given the limited space occupied, reasonable operation cost, and zero-pollutant emission, ozone oxidation can be adapted to retrofit the existing power plant. Thus, a scheme design of simultaneous multi-pollutants removal through O_3 and FGD is attentively advocated in this section by using a 300 MWe boiler as an example.

Fig. 5.1 shows the schematic of simultaneous multi-pollutants removal, coupled with ozone oxidation and alkali solution. High-concentration ozone (with a mass concentration of $80 - 130$ g/m^3 in the balance gas, equaling to a volume share of 3.7% – 6%) generated by an ozone generator, is sent to a convector through a grid porous jet device. This device is placed between the air preheater and electrostatic precipitator with temperature levels around 150 °C, which are optimal for oxidation reactions among O_3, NO_x, and Hg^0. The ozone dosage injected is mainly determined by the NO content in flue gas. With the mole ratio of O_3/NO above 1, NO is usually oxidized into high-valence NO_x (i.e., NO_2, NO_3, and N_2O_5) and Hg^0 is oxidized into Hg^{2+}; these matters are capable of scrubbing, integrated with the absorbability of acid gas of SO_2, HCl, and HF in the alkali solution scrubber. Afterwards, the produced sulfates and nitrates can be extracted and concentrated in the crystallization system and then be sold as industrial raw materials. Meanwhile, Hg^{2+} in the solution can transform into the steady HgS precipitation through the treatment of H_2S gas, thereby avoiding secondary pollution.

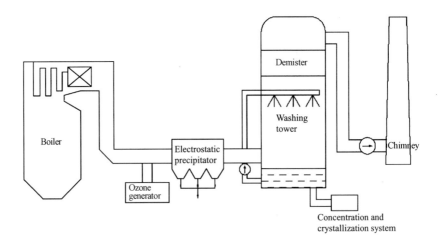

Fig. 5.1   Schematic diagram of the simultaneous removal of multi-pollutants by ozone oxidation

Although here the sole denitration retrofit cost is relatively higher than any other NO_x reduction technologies (typically SCR and SNCR), the present multi-pollutants removal technology focuses on the most effective removal of NO_x, SO_2, Hg^0, HCl, and HF, thereby being acknowledged as a cost-effective, near-zero pollutant emission, co-product reutilization alternative to the development of new multi-pollutants removal technologies. According to our experimental results, the removal efficiencies are over 90% for NO_x, above 99% for SO_2, about 95% for Hg, and over 95% for both HCl and HF. Here the NO_x removal efficiency is also related with combustion control in the furnace. NO_x should be first lowered through approaches such as low-NO_x burners, air-staging combustion, and fuel reburning. For example, with the initial NO_x concentration in the furnace lowered by about $150 - 200$ ppm, the original NO_x emissions of 800 mg/m^3 (at 6% O_2) can be lowered to $300 - 400$ mg/m^3 (at 6% O_2). Subsequently, another $100 - 150$ ppm reduction extent in the remaining NO_x is achieved through ozone oxidation in flue gas, finally resulting in a total NO_x removal efficiency of 93.7%.

It is quite common for denitration to adopt the typical alkali chemicals to absorb NO_x in the tail alkali absorption. The typical alkali chemicals comprise KOH, NaOH, $Ca(OH)_2$, Na_2CO_3, $NaHCO_3$, and so on. Nevertheless, the absorption efficiency is quite low because of the comparatively low reaction activity indexes (definitely shown in Table 5.1) of these alkali chemicals. Considering that NO is hardly soluble in water while its oxidized form of NO_2 has a strong water solubility, NO should be transformed into NO_2 initially and effectively absorbed by alkali solution afterwards.

Table 5.1 Relative value of the reaction activity of various alkali chemicals that absorb NO_x

Alkali chemicals	Relative value
KOH	1
NaOH	0.84
$Ca(OH)_2$	0.8
Na_2CO_3	0.78
K_2CO_3	0.63
$Ba(OH)_2$	0.56
$NaHCO_3$	0.51
$MgCO_3$	0.41
$BaCO_3$	0.4
$CaCO_3$	0.39

Nowadays, the WFGD technology is globally adopted, in which a lime/limestone slurry washing is the most matures and widely used for the coal-fired flue gas desulfurization because of its advantages cost-effective, high-efficient, and abundant raw materials. The simultaneous removal multi-pollutants through ozone oxidation and an alkali solution adsorption can be easily obtained if NO_x, SO_2, H_2S, Hg, and VOCs are sufficiently oxidized. If the FGD system has already been installed in the power plants, the ozone oxidation equipment can be installed before the desulfurization system. The oxidation products and acids in flue gas can be absorbed by a $CaCO_3$ solution. If there is no FGD existing, the ozone oxidation and chemical absorption equipments can be installed after the dust collecting system. To evaluate the simultaneous multi-pollutants removal performance, a pilot-scale ozone oxidation and chemical absorption system has been established with a maximal 300 $N \cdot m^3/h$ flue gas processing capacity, as shown in Fig. 5.2.

(a)   (b)

Fig. 5.2   (a) Ozone oxidation and (b) chemical absorption equipment

As an active molecule but with a relatively long lifespan, Ozone can be generated through discharging and then ejected into flue gas. The conventional operational conditions of the system are flue gas rate of 100 N·m^3/h, flue gas temperature levels of 100 – 300 °C, ozone production of 150 g/h.

5.2   Economic Analysis of the Ozone Generation Technology

The ozone generation technology plays an important role in the simultaneous removal of multi-pollutants. An effective ozone generation method usually corresponds to low energy consumption, which determines mainly the economic feasibility of this technology. Therefore, it is essential for cost-effective purpose to explore new ozone generators. Table 5.2 shows comprehensive comparisons between the commercial and proposed ozone generators.

Figs. 5.3(a) and 5.3(b) compare the ozone generation performance between a commercial ozone generator and the developed one with high frequency and high voltage (listed in Table 5.2). Both the ozone discharge chambers are of the coaxial-cylindrical type. Generally, a commercial ozone generator operate with a voltage of 4 – 5 kV, frequency of 1000 – 3000 Hz, and an ozone yield rates below 111.11 g/(kW·h). As for us, the ozone generation experiments were conducted with a voltage of 2.4 – 3.4 kV, frequency of 7.47 kHz, and an ozone yield rate below 163.81 g/(kW·h). As shown in Figs. 5.3(a) and 5.3(b), the ozone yield increases with the oxygen flow rate, despite a continuous decrease appearing in the ozone concentration, because of the oxygen dilution. Results in our generator are definitely twice higher than those of the commercial one, not only in the ozone concentration but also in the ozone yield.

Table 5.2   Parameter comparisons of various ozone generation technologies (per unit)

Ozone generation technologies	Dry air source		Oxygen	
	Content (g/m^3)	Yield rate (g/(kW·h))	Content (g/m^3)	Yield rate (g/(kW·h))
Commercial product	5.64 – 11.55	<55.56	16.55–60.7	<111.11
High-frequency high-voltage discharge	2.6 – 5.3	2.56 – 43.62	24.1–76.8	70.56 – 158.32
High-frequency high-voltage discharge (SF$_6$ added)	6.11–12.46	6.02 – 102.51	—	—
Experimental data from Samaranayake[1,2]	<21.4	<100.0	<21.4	<200.0
Pulse discharge (single channel)	7.1 – 39.3	294.0 – 407.8	11.8 – 57.9	493.46 – 1081.09
Pulse discharge (double channel)	2.9 – 27.7	163.00 – 271.39	12.1 – 48.0	467.68 – 700.88

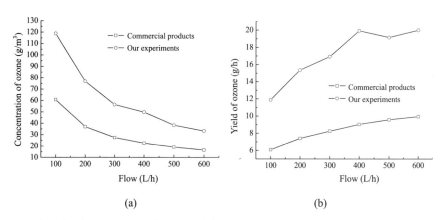

(a)   (b)

Fig. 5.3   Ozone concentration (a) and yield (b) variation with flow (oxygen source)

Using a ns-grade power supply to generate ozone is firstly reported by Samaranayake's group [1,2]. The discharge chamber used was a line (helix)-cylinder type and experiments were conducted with a 1 L/min flow rate, 1-mm electrode gap, pulse repetition frequency below 500 pps, peak voltage below 60 kV, and pulse width of 120 ns, yielding a 200 g/(kW·h) ozone supply. In our ozone generator, some modifications were carried out to improve the ozone generation performance, compared with the generator of Samaranayake's group [1,2]. In detail, a flat discharge chamber was adopted and the operational parameters of our ozone generator were the pulse repetition frequency below 300 Hz, peak voltage below 60 kV, pulse width of 300 – 500 ns, and ozone yield of 493.46 – 1081.09 g/(kW·h). The result comparison between our pulse discharge ozone generator and that of Samaranayake's group [1,2] is presented in Fig. 5.4. Obviously, results from the two research groups are quite different. For the pulse discharge ozone generator modified by our group, its performance is much better than that of the generator in [1,2]. In detail, both the ozone concentration and yield rate greatly increase (see results in both Figs. 5.3 and 5.4) and the needed voltage of the discharge chamber is much lower when the flat type of ozone generator is applied, in comparison with the line (helix)-cylinder type in [1,2]. Therefore, the lifespan and reliability are improved clearly. Analytically, the ozone generator with flat discharge chamber appears as a promising cost-effective, economical, and reliable alternative.

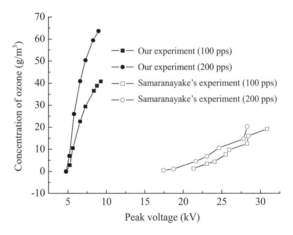

Fig. 5.4 Ozone concentration variation with peak voltage (oxygen source)

Note: Our experiments: 1 L/min flow rate and 1 mm gap; Samaranayake's experiments: 1 L/min flow rate and 1 mm gap

5.3 Economic Analysis of the O_3 and FGD System

For the most strictest NO_x emission standards of power plants in China (i.e., the permissible NO_x emissions of 100 mg/m^3 (at 6% O_2) for most of coal-fired boilers, as of July 1, 2014), it is very tough to satisfy the demand with the help of those existing deNO$_x$ technologies (such as SCR and SNCR). This means that a good chance for adopt the advanced and promising O_3 and FGD technology appears, owing to a variety of advantages, namely, the most effective approach to achieve multi-pollutants removal of NO_x, SO_2, Hg, HCl, and HF in a aqueous scrubbers, more economical, lower retrofit and running cost. As mentioned previously, in general, above 90% of NO_x, more than 95% of SO_2, and no less than 85% of Hg can be removed, based on the testing results of some industrial applications. And the high NO_x abatement efficiency is actually attained by the combination of combustion control in the furnace and ozone oxidation in the flue gas; this combination strategy can greatly reduce the O_3 consumption, thereby saving sharply the cost in NO_x abatement.

Take a 300 MWe unit with typical operational parameters and multi-pollutants emission levels, Table 5.3 lists the O_3 requirement and energy consumption for the proposed multi-pollutants simultaneous removal technology, based on our calculations. Reducing NO_x emissions from 600 to 400 mg/m³ (at 6% O_2) necessitates an O_3 consumption of 257.1 kg/h, which exceeds a little the output of a 200 kg/h large-scale ozone generator for sale on the current market. Two types of gas sources, i.e., air and oxygen, can be used in ozone generators. When air is used, the N_2 in air will consume most of the energy during the discharge process (6814.29 kW) because of high-energy consumption in the ozone generation, which can reach up to 26.5 kW per kg ozone. The unit flue gas energy consumption therefore reaches up to 5.68 W/(N·m³), which accounts for 2.27% of the total electricity generation. Using oxygen as the gas source, although additional energy consumption needs in preparing the oxygen source, the energy consumption of ozone generation significantly reduces to a minimum of 6 kW per kg ozone in the present market. Consequently, the unit flue gas energy consumption reduces greatly to 1.91 W/(N·m³), which accounts for only 0.76% of the electric power generation. This means that 66.5% of the power consumption can be saved by using oxygen instead of air as a gas source in the ozone generation process. Obviously, the key factor to reducing the operational cost in practical applications is to choose oxygen as the gas source and to develop a large-scale ozone generator with low power consumption.

Obviously, it is a better choice to adopt the ozone oxidation technology integrated with NO_x control strategies during the fuel combustion process (such as low-NO_x burners, air-staging combustion, and fuel reburning) for a reasonable investment. From Table 5.4 compares various schemes with ozone application for

Table 5.3 Energy consumption calculation of O_3 generated in a 300 MWe unit

Unit capability (MWe)	300	Mole ratio of O_3/NO	1
Flue gas volume $((N \cdot m^3)/h)$	1.20E+06	Content of Hg $(mg/(N \cdot m^3))$	0.03
Initial concentration of NO_x $(mg/(N \cdot m^3))$	600	Content of SO_2 (ppm)	100
Emission concentration of NO_x $(mg/(N \cdot m^3))$	400	Required content of O_3 (kg/h)	257

	Produce O_3 by air	Produce O_3 by oxygen
Ozone concentration $(g/(N \cdot m^3))$	20	130
Gas volume $((N \cdot m^3)/h)$	12857	1978
Energy consumption per kg O_3 $(kW/kg\ O_3)$	26.5	6
Energy consumption 1 (kW)	6814	1543
Energy consumption of each $m^3\ O_2$ $(kW/m^3\ O_2)$	—	0.38
Energy consumption 2 (kW)	—	752
Total energy consumption (kW)	6814	2294
Unit fume energy consumption $(W/(N \cdot m^3))$	5.68	1.91
Ratio of power generation (%)	2.27	0.76

Table 5.4 Investment comparison of the power consumption of the separate techniques by using O_3 and the method combined with furnace techniques

Initial concentration of NO $(mg/(N \cdot m^3))$	600		
	O_3 only	O_3+OFA	O_3+reburning
Removal efficiency in the furnace (%)	0	30	50
Concentration of NO during O_3 treatment process $(mg/(N \cdot m^3))$	600	420	300
Final emission concentration $(mg/(N \cdot m^3))$	200	200	200
The overall removal efficiency of NO_x (%)	66.67	66.67	66.67
Investment (ten thousand yuan)	3857	2121	964
Unit investment (yuan/kW)	129	71	32
Required amount of O_3 (kg/h)	514	283	128
Total energy consumption (kW)	4589	2524	1147
Ratio of power generation (%)	1.53	0.84	0.38

flue gas treatment. It can be seen that using only ozone is less economical than the combination method with OFA or reburning. Clearly, the flue gas energy consumption for the NO_x reduction is quite different, ozone plus reburning, ozone plus OFA, and ozone level at 0.38, 0.84, and 1.53% of the total power generation, respectively, for a same NO_x removal efficiency of 66.67%.

Additionally, the investment and operational cost between O_3 and other existing technologies for NO_x and SO_2 removal needs to be compared. Their comparisons are listed in Table 5.5, in which the assumed emission concentration of NO_x and SO_2 without any removal process are 800 and 2000 mg/m^3 (at 6% O_2), respectively.

WFGD is the most widely used and mature SO_2 removal technology, with a desulfurization efficiency of over 95% and SO_2 removal cost at about 839 yuan/ton [3–8]. The most efficient NO_x removal technology at present is SCR, which achieved a denitrition efficiency of 80% – 95% but with a high investment of about 100 – 200 yuan/kW and expensive operational cost of about 4.3 points/(kW·h). Even the United States considers SCR is too expensive so as to explore a new low-cost denitrition method. OFA is one of the mature denitration technologies with the lowest investment and operational cost, which can reach a denitrification efficiency of 30% with an investment cost of only 15 – 20 yuan/kW and hardly needs an additional running cost. Ultra-fine pulverized-coal reburning technology with a NO_x removal efficiency of 30% – 50%, has a slightly higher investment of 20 – 30 yuan/kW because of its additional ultra-fine powder preparation system, whose running cost is mainly attributed to the 0.8 yuan/(kW·h) power consumption of the mills. The electron beam technology can attain a desulfuration and denitrition efficiency of 80% and 10% – 20%, with an investment of 600 yuan/kW and running cost of 0.76 points/(kW·h) [9]. Despite its relatively high investment, this technology is currently used in commercial operations of a thermal power plant in Hangzhou in China because of its ability of removing NO_x and SO_2 simultaneously.

Now the attention is focused on the combination of O_3 application and OFA on the basis of WFGD. The initial investment is 120 yuan/kW, which can be reduced further to 70 yuan/kW if combined with the reburning technology, instead of OFA. If ozone oxidation combined with reburning and WFGD, an 80% denitrification efficiency, 95% desulfurization efficiency, and 85% mercury removal efficiency can be achieved simultaneously. The resulted NO_x emissions drop to 160 mg/m^3 (at 6% O_2), almost equaling to the levels after a SCR process.

Table 5.5　Comparison of investments and running costs of various technologies

Project	Unit	OFA	Pulverized coal reburning	SNCR	SCR	WFGD
NO_x emission	$mg/(N \cdot m^3)$	560	400–560	480–560	40–160	800
SO_2 emission	$mg/(N \cdot m^3)$	2000	2000	2000	2000	100
NO_x removal	%	30	30–50	30–40	80–95	No
SO_2 removal	%	no	no	no	no	95
Hg removal	%	no	no	no	—	No
Investment	yuan/kW	15–20	20–30	50–170	200	280
Operating costs	Point/(kW·h)	≈ 0	0.8	0.4	2–4.3	1.5

Project	WFGD	Electron beam	WFGD basis		reburning+SNCR
			O_3+OFA	O_3+reburning	
NO_x emission	800	640–720	160	160	250
SO_2 emission	100	400	100	100	2,000
NO_x removal	No	10–20	80	80	68.75
SO_2 removal	95	80	95	95	No
Hg removal	No	no	85	85	No
Investment	280	600	120	70	90–100
Operating costs	1.5	0.76	0.3	0.2	0.5

Note: The initial emission concentration of NO_x and SO_2 is 800 and 2000 mg/(N·m³), respectively

Both O_3 oxidization and e-beam technologies belong to the electro-catalytic category. However, e-beam discharges in the entire flue gas. The inactive N_2 and CO_2 in flue gas consume a lot of energy. However, O_3 only discharges a small dosage of oxygen or air. Therefore, both the discharge efficiency and electrode lifespan in O_3 generation are superior to those in the electron-beam preparation. The energy consumption of the electron beam levels at 6.3 W/(N·m³) when achieving the same NO_x emission levels released by the Chengdu Thermal Power Plant in China. On the contrary, O_3 oxidation only consumes 0.83 – 0.96 W/(N·m³), saving more than 80% power consumption [9], compared with the aforementioned e-beam method. Definitely, ozone oxidation combined with OFA or reburning, coupled with WFGD system, is approved as a promising cost-effective multi-pollutants removal method.

5.4　Summary

This chapter is attentively employed to present an engineering design of a multi-pollutants removal technology incorporated with ozone oxidization and alkali solution adsorption. An economic analysis of O_3 oxidization combined with the existing desulfurization (mainly WFGD) and denitrification (OFA, reburning, SCR, and so on) technologies was also provided. A pilot-scale ozone oxidation system combined with chemical absorption was established to process a maximal 300 N·m³/h flue gas flow. Operational conditions of flue gas capacity 100 N·m³/h, gas temperatures 100 – 300 °C, and ozone output 150 g/h were preferred. In the ozone generation technology aspect, both the high-frequency and high-voltage discharge method and the pulse discharge method can substantially increase ozone concentration and yield. The economic analysis of multi-pollutants simultaneous removal with ozone oxidization and alkali solution adsorption for a typical 300 MWe unit boiler suggests that: (i) oxygen needs be the gas source for the ozone generation, instead of air, so as to reduce sharply the operation energy consumption; and (ii) ozone oxidation must combine with OFA or reburning, coupled with WFGD system, is approved as a promising cost-effective multi-pollutants removal method.

References

[1] Samaranayake WJM, Miyahara Y, Namihira T, Katsuki S, Sakugawa T, Hackam R, *et al.* Pulsed streamer discharge characteristics of ozone production in dry air. IEEE Transsctions on Dielectrics and Electrical Insulation, 2000(7):254–260.

[2] Samaranayake WJM, Miyahara Y, Namihira T, Katsuki S, Hackam R, Akiyama H. Ozone production using pulsed dielectric barrier discharge in oxygen. IEEE Transsctions on Dielectrics and Electrical Insulation, 2000(7):849–854.

[3] Zeng TH. Analysis on design and operation of the absorber system in wet FGD plant. Electric Power Environmental Protection, 2002(18):5–9.

[4] He ZH, Li J. Control technologies of SO_2 pollution from coal-fired power plants and their application in China. Electric Power Environmental Protection, 2002(18):4–7.

[5] Wang D, Li ZJ, Lin R. Operational economic analysis on sea-water desulfurization system of Unit 4 in Shenzhen Mawan Power Plant. Electric Power Environmental Protection, 2002(18):15–17.

[6] Chen DB. Application of pure seawater FGD process in coal-fired power station. Electric Power Environmental Protection, 2002(18):8–12.

[7] Wu D, Chen BP. NADS ammonia-fertilizer method: A new desulfurization technology for a thermal power plant. Coal Processing and Comprehensive

Utilization, 2001(5):50–53.

[8] Zhang W. Wet FGD system applied in American Centralia Power Plant. International Electric Power for China, 2004(8):55–58.

[9] Tai DR, Han BB. Advances on industrial demonstration for electron beam desulfuration technology of flue gas. Chinese Journal of Environmental Engineering, 1999(7):125–135.

Index